DREAMTIGERS

DREAMTIGERS

BY

Jorge Luis Borges

Translated from EL HACEDOR (*The Maker*)
by Mildred Boyer and Harold Morland
Preface by Victor Lange
Introduction by Miguel Enguídanos

A Dutton *Paperback*

New York
E. P. DUTTON & CO., INC.

This paperback edition of

"Dreamtigers"

First published 1970 by E. P. Dutton & Co., Inc.
All rights reserved. Printed in the U.S.A.

Copyright © 1964 by Jorge Luis Borges.
Published by special arrangement with
the University of Texas Press, Austin.

Published simultaneously in Canada by Clarke,
Irwin & Company Limited, Toronto and Vancouver.

SBN 0-525-47269-X

JORGE LUIS BORGES is among the most original of contemporary Spanish-American writers, and he has been called "one of the most solitary, intelligent, and sensitive souls of our time." Born in Buenos Aires in 1899, he was educated in Europe. After his return to Argentina at the age of twenty-two he was associated with the rebellious vanguardist poets. He has lived obscurely and tranquilly as a municipal librarian in Buenos Aires. He is now director of the National Library of Argentina and Professor of English Literature at the University of Buenos Aires.

The translators, Mildred Vinson Boyer and Harold Morland, are both accomplished scholars in Spanish and enthusiastic readers of Borges. Miss Boyer is Associate Professor of Romance Languages at The University of Texas, and a student of eighteenth-century Spanish literature. Mr. Morland, for several years deputy principal of Newland Park College, Buckinghamshire, England, is the author of several volumes of poetry and translations from modern Spanish poets. Victor Lange, who wrote the Preface to this paperback edition of *Dreamtigers*, is Professor of Modern Languages at Princeton University, and Miguel Enguídanos, who provided the Introduction, is Professor of Romance Languages at The University of Texas.

DREAMTIGERS was first published in 1964 as one of the Texas Pan-American Series of The University of Texas Press.

Contents

Preface

Those who like to think of contemporary literature as being primarily concerned with elucidating our social and political alternatives, or, on the other hand, as exercises in aesthetic detachment have found in Borges' work too little commitment to the concrete issues of today and too great a fascination with metaphysics and the metaphorical magic of language. The distinction is, of course, a blunt and rigid one that does justice neither to the artistry of moralists such as Kafka or Camus nor to the sense of existential urgency in the work of Musil, Valéry, and Beckett or, indeed, of Borges himself. These are the consummate artists of our time, the creators of a sceptical yet impassioned sensibility, the portrayers of the modern mind that is no longer happily at home in a familiar and reassuring world, but has turned upon itself in search of an understanding of its precarious capacities.

The stature of a writer, the force and integrity of his appeal, perhaps the measure of his greatness, are at all times the result of the unmistakable substance of his person and of his critical awareness of the age and the society that sustain him. But it is no less the sign of a compelling achievement that it should draw its strength, beyond the immediacy of experienced life, from a commitment to the traditions of thought and form from which it derives its convictions. Jorge Luis Borges, one of the three or four magisterial figures of contemporary literature, is an Argentinian: he was born in Buenos Aires in 1899 and has remained, despite—or because of—long periods of travel and residence abroad, deeply absorbed in his native culture: "I felt Buenos Aires," he wrote in 1943,

> "this city I thought was my past
> is really my future, my present;
> the years I have lived in Europe are illusory,
> I have always been (and will be) in Buenos Aires."
>
> *(Poemas, 1923–1958)*

Yet Borges' personal and public attachment to Argentina, however strongly it may emerge from his writing—from his literary and historical essays as well as his poetry and fiction—is altogether illuminated and even transcended by his affinity to English and American literature and to European philosophy, history, and art.

From his early poetry (*Fervor de Buenos Aires*, 1923) to those sparse but fascinating collections of tales and reflections (*Historia universal de la infamia*, 1935; *Ficciones*, 1944; *El Aleph*, 1949; *Otras inquisiciones*, 1952) Borges has been preoccupied with the place, in a universe whose features are elusive, of the human being anguished by the corroding experience of time and forever attempting to determine the character of a world in which actuality and appearance cannot be distinguished. Like that of other exemplary writers of our time, Borges' work turns upon an almost obsessive curiosity as to the character and scope of our perception and knowledge. To know the world is for Borges, beyond all sensuous experience, to contemplate the countless theories of knowledge offered by philosophers and poets, the projections and fictions of the inexhaustible human imagination. Reality, whether actual or historical or speculative, offers him the materials from which, throughout its history, the mind has constructed those systems of judgment and faith, and those dreams and aspirations which, once invented, remain the irrefutable hypotheses of being. The presence of these fictions offers us the only evidence of world, the only substance of truth with which we can and should be concerned. Life and its mirror-image in the imagination are indistinguishable, object and subject are one, reality and dream flow one into the other.

So involuted and self-destructive a perspective might well seem the melancholy conclusion of a sentimental mind. But Borges' work elaborates with relentless precision and unflinching lucidity the compulsions of intellect and moral intelligence with which we must confront and describe—"in a basely romantic age"—a universe that cannot be reduced to human dimensions and that must be endured in its absurd irrationality. The tenor of Borges' writings is, therefore, not lyrical but objective: his insistent question—whether or not, in such an indeterminable universe, it is possible ever to fix and comprehend identity—is not concerned with the range of our psychological—or social or existential—self. The self, he argues, is poorly defined if we think of it as a fixed potential, and it is a pity that the literature of our time should tend to perpetuate such a seductive form of delusion: "Man's character and its variations constitute the essential theme of the novel of our time; the lyric is the complacent magnification of amorous fortunes or misfortunes; the philosophies of Heidegger or Jaspers transform each one of us into the interesting interlocutor of a secret and continuous dialogue with nothingness or with divinity; these disciplines, which may be formally admirable, foster the illusion of the self that Vedānta condemns as a capital error. They may play at desperation and anguish, but at bottom they flatter the vanity; in that sense, they are immoral ("For Bernard Shaw," *Other Inquisitions*).

What Borges attempts to represent throughout his work is not any differentiated ego but the sceptical mind that is fascinated by an unending compulsion to isolate and define moments of experience in which the presumed identity of self, of here and now, can be fathomed and recognized as a tragic illusion.

The ancestors of this philosophy of detachment and self-doubt seem present at every moment of Borges' reflections: the voice of Pascal or Berkeley, of Hume and Kant join to liberate the spirit of man from the confining reality of this world; Heraclitus, Spinoza, Schopenhauer, and Nietzsche testify to the eternal recurrence in which the single act becomes myth and symbol. Yet there is in Borges' writings no coherent attempt at elaborating his own or others' philosophical positions; indeed, his distaste for any supposition of meaning leads him to insist that all systems of thought, all philosophical or theological speculations are merely evidence of that desperate compulsion to reflect upon our own delusions; as such they are instances of fantastic literature. And it is the agony of philosophical perplexity, those moments at which "the scruples and wonders of thought" appear at their most illusory, that are the matter of Borges' art.

But if the history of the mind offers Borges the inexhaustible subject matter of his narratives, its unceasing preoccupation with the indeterminable borders between appearance and reality, truth and deception must be meticulously elaborated; as all knowledge is relative, its assertions and pretensions must be recorded with the most careful respect for their momentary claims. The immense and almost ceremonious care with which Borges in his stories marshalls recondite learning and with which he fabricates learned evidence suggests the irony with which he treats all claims to truth and points to his fundamental conviction of the fictitious character of reality. A multitude of curious archeological facts and literary references, strange occurrences and historical and personal reminiscences are pedantically related in order to conjure up for the reader a universe composed of information, hearsay, and fiction which, with its baffling refractions and echo-effects conveys something of the labyrinthine character of reality itself.

Learning is the material as well as the topic of Borges' art, and he himself is the conspicuous example of a *poeta doctus* no less impressive than Valéry or Pound, who has spent a lifetime "not so much devoted to living as to belles lettres and, occasionally, to the perplexities of metaphysics" ("A New Refutation of Time"). His work revolves characteristically and single-mindedly around the range and validity of the creative act: it is, in a sense, a continuing monologue on the feasibility of making assertions about the world, and its persona is always the writer meditating on the act of writing. Borges belongs among those radically self-conscious writers who, like Baudelaire and Mallarmé or, in our own time, Beckett or Nabokov, attempt, in a state of immobility that is the price of rarefied insight and memory, and in terse structures of the imagination, to mirror an absurd creation. Writers write, Borges argues, to prove their own dubious substance, to free themselves in some way or other from that sense of unreality and vacuity that haunts them. Their relationship to the world of facts and verifiable reality is bound to be paradoxical: they must in their poetry at once affirm and parody the meaningless evidence of the world. For the essential character of the universe, Borges has frequently reiterated, is its emptiness: whatever the spectacular doings of its inhabitants, whatever the subtlety of their acts of self-justification, the accounts of these adventures are mere fictions and equivocal metaphors.

It is for this reason that the nature and scope of language is a central issue of Borges' stories, of his poetry and critical reflections. He is, of course, a craftsman of the most severe precision, a master of exactitude and reduction. Yet with all the measured discipline of his manner and the achieved casualness of a De Quincey or a Stevenson, he is far from accepting the classical view of language as a system of successive, causally related statements. Assuming, as he does, that the universe is unexplainable and that all our reflections upon it contain within them their own improbability, he is resolved in his speech to undermine all facile assumptions of sequentiality and to demonstrate the essentially poetic, allegorical, or metaphorical character of the word. In order to convey the experience of fluidity and interlocking correspondences, he produces—much like Musil, that other sceptic of the unqualified utterance—within a sentence or paragraph the double tension of assertion and denial, of statement and counterstatement, of assurance and doubt. His suspicion toward language stems from a belief that it simplifies reality, that terms such as space or time, matter or spirit, can be no more than misleading approximations of the ineffable complexity of our own speculations. Yet "this will be our destiny," he says in an early essay, "to give ourselves to syntax, to its treacherous linkage, to imprecision, to perhaps, to the exaggerated emphasis, to buts, to the hemisphere of lies and shadows in our sayings" ("The Language of Argentinians"). Speech is, then, ultimately bound to fail; however cautious, allusive, it can only conceal its inadequacy. Again and again Borges speaks of his fascination with the attempts of past philosophers—Spinoza or Leibniz or Locke —to create an artificial and universal language. They have all been in vain; yet even these uncompromising efforts merely testify to the desperate conclusions that we can transcend our treacherous speech only in silence or by finding a transparent language or a word which has the magic capacity to grasp and order the world.

The "Parable of the Palace," one of the finest stories in *Dreamtigers*, elaborates this most fundamental of Borges' concepts: the poet is here cut down by the executioner for being able to contain the universe in one verse, perhaps a single image—"The text has been lost. There are some who contend that it consisted of a single line; others say it had but a single word. The truth, the incredible truth, is that in the poem stood the enormous palace, entire and minutely detailed, with each illustrious porcelain and every sketch on every porcelain and the shadows and the light of the twilights and each unhappy or joyous moment of the glorious dynasties of mortals, gods, and dragons who had dwelled in it from the interminable past." The emperor orders the poet's execution—"You have robbed me of my palace!" The poet's work was the great Fall: for a moment he had assumed the role of God and usurped His creation. But by his legendary act he had also created an inextinguishable desire in his descendants who "still seek, nor will they find, the one word that contains the universe." This Kafka-like theme is varied in the poem "The Moon," in which a man

> Conceived the unconscionable plan
> Of making an abridgement of the universe
> In a single book . . .

He succeeded; but as he lifted up his eyes he became aware that he had forgotten the moon: in transmuting life into words, this is to say, the essence is always lost—that absent essence, that "nothingness" to which Borges, like Mallarmé, forever returns.

The universe conceived as "The God's Script" and nature as the puzzling system of hieroglyphic approximations of an absolute mind is a topos which Borges derives from the romantics: "What type of sentence (I asked myself) will an absolute mind construct? I considered that even in the human languages there is no proposition that does not imply the entire universe; to say *the tiger* is to say the tigers that begot it, the deer and turtles devoured by it, the grass on which the deer fed, the earth that was mother to the grass, the heaven that gave birth to the earth. I considered that in the language of a god every word would enunciate that infinite concatenation of facts, and not in an implicit but in an explicit manner, and not progessively but instantaneously. In time, the notion of a divine sentence seemed puerile or blasphemous. A god, I reflected, ought to utter only a single word and in that word absolute fullness. No word uttered by him can be inferior to the universe or less than the sum total of time. Shadows or simulacra of that single word equivalent to a language and to all a language can embrace are the poor and ambitious human words, *all, world, universe.*"

The world as book, as idea or dream is a notion that stems from a venerable tradition: the mystics as well as Schopenhauer and the symbolist poets—Mallarmé's sentence: "tout au monde existe pour aboutir à un livre"—have asserted their belief (in which Borges concurs) that the universe is a vast vocabulary of being, that words, far from reflecting an immanent if intangible essence, themselves are an irrefutable reality. To words, "blasphemous as it may seem, are reduced Achilles, Peer Gynt, Robinson Crusoe and the Baron de Charlus. To that, too, the powerful men who ruled the earth; Alexander is a series of words and Attila is another . . ." (an interview in *La Nación*, March 30, 1948). In another of those delicate and moving pieces in *Dreamtigers*, the dying poet, contemplating the flower of which he had once spoken in immortal lines, comes to realize "that the rose was to be found in its own eternity and not in his words; and that we may mention or allude to a thing, but not express it; and that the tall, proud volumes . . . were not—as his vanity had dreamed—a mirror of the world, but rather one thing more added to the world ("A Yellow Rose"). Art, Borges reminds us often enough, cannot "express." Indeed, he suggests that to the belief that art is expression, "or to a deformation of this exigency, we owe the worst literature of our time." And if, he adds, "sometimes I, too, sought expression, I know now that my gods grant me no more than allusion or mention" ("Prologue," *A Personal Anthology*).

Literature, then, that "metaphor of the universe," offers us projects of the mind in which space and time can be shown in their ultimate irrelevance: it is the poet's chance to fill this immense void of the universe with elaborately constructed fictions that offer subtle but compelling demonstrations of the delusion that determines our thinking. The creation of quasi-logical propositions and the rendering of incidents and figures that are minutely documented and reassuringly detailed is the chief purpose of Borges' narrative technique. Yet the fantastic structures of Borges' stories, conjured as though by magic or sleight of hand, are the product of acts of calculated deception. What is in one breath stated as corroborated fact is at the same time obscured and blurred by doubts, denials, and open questions. The image of the labyrinth, the discontinuous pseudo-plot of the dream, and the device and metaphor of the mirror are the appropriate structural and thematic signatures of Borges' work; they are the aesthetic signals by which the presumption of order and logic is not so much created as denied. They create at the same time that illusion of artificial spaces within which each narrated object and each reported statement serves only as an instrument of refraction whose place and identity cannot be specified. The countless mirrors in Borges' stories do not clarify but confuse; they produce in the reader a feeling of vertigo, and, as they demonstrate by their infinite repetitions a sense of nonreality and nonidentity, they take on an altogether terrifying and ominous character. As a child, he reports in "The Draped Mirrors," he felt before large mirrors that "horror of a spectral duplication or multiplication of reality." And, still more specifically, the poem "Mirrors" speaks of the shock that these "impenetrable crystals" produced in him.

> I ask myself what whim of fate
> Made me so fearful of a glancing mirror.

> Mirrors in metal, and the masked
> Mirror of mahogany that in its mist
> Of the red twilight hazes
> The face that is gazed on as it gazes,

> I see them as infinite, elemental
> Executors of an ancient pact,
> To multiply the world like the act
> Of begetting. Sleepless. Bringing doom.

> They prolong this hollow, unstable world
> In their dizzying spider's-web. . . .

In the hallway of "The Library of Babel"—another of Borges' many-faceted image-complexes suggesting infinite multiplicity—"there is a mirror which faithfully duplicates all appearances. Men usually infer from this mirror that the

Library is not infinite (if it really were, why this illusory duplication?); I prefer to dream that its polished surfaces represent and promise the infinite . . ." The space in which this impalpable play of mirror images produces its unending repetition of treacherous appearances is a labyrinth which, like the ever-receding perspective of the law courts in Kafka's *Trial*, permits no orientation or escape. The terraces of the palace of the Yellow Emperor (in "Parable of the Palace") descend "like the steps of an almost measureless amphitheater, to a paradise or garden whose metal mirrors and intricate juniper hedges already prefigured the labyrinth." Houses, galleries, winding staircases, or interminable streets offer an intricate architecture of phantasmagoric hallucinations and insistent metaphors of chaos and infinity.

If mirrors and labyrinths dissolve the presumption of spatial order, it is in the boundless and fluctuating universe of the dream that the intersecting of reality and appearance is most strikingly represented in Borges' fiction: the world as dream, the real and the dreamed as one, reality as a configuration of dreams—these are ideas that recur throughout Borges' work and are made concrete in his plots and images. Reality dissolves in appearances and these in turn may be no more than fanciful pretensions of the imagination. In that superb parable, "Everything and Nothing," the world is seen as the divine dream, containing figures and constellations that can at best be aware of their own fictitious role in the universe. What we take as reality is merely one of the projections of this universal dream; and that no-man's-land of experience where memory and speculation, individual encounters and collective myths meet, affords us an inkling of the infinity of time and space. Time and space are the crutches of a self-deceived mind—concepts that must be seen in their irrelevance, however haunting our dependence upon them, if we are not to remain entrapped in the fallacy of self and identity.

But, not unlike God, the poet is the creator of hallucinatory dreams, uncertain and in deluded search of "the moment in which a man once and for all knows who he is" ("Biography of Tadio Isidoro Cruz [1829–1874]"). Yet, if there can be no "forever," we are ineluctably embedded in time: "Time is the substance of which I am made. Time is a river which sweeps me along, but I am the river; it is a tiger which mangles me, but I am the tiger; it is a fire which consumes me, but I am the fire. The world, unfortunately, is real; I, unfortunately, am Borges" ("A New Refutation of Time").

By an extraordinary variety of devices, Borges thus undermines all assumptions of stability: mirror and dreams are only the most obvious; the deliberate mixing of historical data and fictitious counter-information is another. Borges' own personal experiences are imperceptibly blurred by imagined and invented elaborations; the evidence of established scholarship and of well-known authorities seems to give concreteness to an altogether fanciful tale; familiar names become images, quotations are invented, puzzling conclusions are drawn from commonplace theories. The real and the fictional shade one into the other in an aesthetic game that offers enough tantalizing clues to remind us of its allegorical or symbolic character: "For myth," he concludes in the "Parable of Cervantes and Don Quixote," "is at the beginning of literature, and also at its end."

Borges' narratives, then, are thought-games about an infinite and always delusive universe, fictions in which arguments, subtle changes in pace, color, and perspective disintegrate the objective world. Unreality, indeed, is the condition of art, and art, we are reminded, offers us the only means by which the all-consuming search for identity can be represented, and by which, at the same time, it can be discredited as a "circular delirium," an existential delusion. In "Everything and Nothing" Borges reflects on the fate of the arch-poet: "There was no one in him; behind his face . . . and his words . . . there was nothing but a little chill, a dream not dreamed by anyone." He is haunted by "the habit of pretending that he was someone, so it would not be discovered that he was no one." He is overcome by a sense of unreality at being all his imagined figures, and turns away from poetry altogether. But as he faced God and now demanded to be himself, the voice in the whirlwind replied, " 'Neither am I one self; I dreamed the world as you dreamed your work, my Shakespeare, and among the shapes of my dream are you, who, like me, are many persons—and none.' "

It would be a mistake to think of Borges' work as being preoccupied with an effort, so common to much contemporary literature, at exploring and defining the individual self and its capacities for coping with a given private and social setting. If Borges represents the complexities and paradoxes of self, he does so with a mixture of melancholy and intellectual assurance: "Borges and I" represents the classic formulation of his conviction that the self is multifarious, that its countless reflections and projections give it reality as well as iridescence. Borges' self confronts his mirror-image, and little by little the living Borges yields to the other I, "well aware of his perverse habit of falsifying and exaggerating." "I live, I allow myself to live, so that Borges may contrive his literature and that literature justifies my existence. I do not mind confessing that he has managed to write some worthwhile pages, but those pages cannot save me, perhaps because the good part no longer belongs to anyone, not even to the other one, but rather to the Spanish language or to tradition."

Rimbaud's *"moi, c'est l'autre,"* the dissociation of the self and the counter-voice, or Musil's figure, in his *Mann ohne Eigenschaften (The Man Without Qualities)*, of a mind constantly specifying its own indeterminacy, are echoed and paraphrased throughout Borges' work. He is the creator of fictions that momentarily fill the universal void, a poet who is a "calculating hallucinator" and who, like God, gives shape to his reflections upon an immeasurable void. God himself, we learn from "Paradiso, XXXI, 108" is "broken and scattered abroad," a "lost face" that has produced a faceless humanity: "Perhaps a feature of the crucified face lurks in every mirror; perhaps the face died, was erased, so that God may be all of us. Who knows but that tonight we may see it in the labyrinth of dreams, and tomorrow not know we saw it."

Dreamtigers is perhaps Borges' most appealing as well as his most characteristic work: of all his books, he confesses in the "Epilogue," "none . . . is as personal as the straggling collection mustered for this hodge-podge, precisely because it abounds in reflections and interpolations." Its original Spanish title, *El hacedor*, suggests the essence of his creative principle: the making of a work of art, of a book which, like Mallarmé's *Le Livre*, is a mirror of life, a parable of the greater creation. It is altogether an account, in brief but radiant crystallizations of the mind, of that descent into memory "which seemed to him endless, and up from that vertigo he succeeded in bringing forth a forgotten recollection that shone like a coin under the rain, perhaps because he had never looked at it, unless in a dream" ("The Maker").

Whether in prose or poetry, it is Borges' ultimate purpose to achieve not a mystical and irrational surrender to an inscrutable chaos, but, on the contrary, the clarity of perception that comes from reflection as well as the meticulous making of models. What Borges offers us are poems and narratives that articulate the nature of our human situation. His achievement is that of a writer, "who in a century that adores 'the chaotic idols of blood, earth and passion' always preferred the lucid pleasures of thought and the secret adventures of order" ("Valéry as Symbol," *Other Inquisitions*). He is a superb artist, who draws on life and books, on the sight of tigers and the moon, on the experiences of poets and philosophers: "Few things have happened to me more worth remembering than Schopenhauer's thought or the music of England's words," he writes in the "Epilogue."

If, like many of his contemporaries, Borges returns again and again to the tragic themes of human solitude and the limitation of our capacity to comprehend the spectacles of the universe, he conveys at the same time the inestimable range of meanings and of recurring patterns of experience that are visible in the mirror image of ourselves.

VICTOR LANGE

Princeton University
February, 1970

xxii

Introduction

Jorge Luis Borges arrived in Austin in September, 1961. The plane that brought him flew for some hours on the edge of a terrible hurricane, the same storm that destroyed several towns along the Texas coast. The placid librarian and University of Buenos Aires professor could not fail to feel on that occasion—as he told us later—a mixture of misgiving and excitement. Texas was for him an epic-laden dream. When the dream came true that September day, it seemed the elements had conspired to give him a heroic reception. Once the first Homeric enthusiasms were over, Borges settled down to the ordinary routine of a visiting professor.

He was with us until the end of January, 1962. He taught courses—on Lugones and Argentine poetry; he gave lectures —Walt Whitman, Macedonio Fernández, and Cansinos-Asséns; and he lived day by day with the group in this university whose interests are the literature, history, and life of our Latin American neighbors. To evoke the impression he made in the many hours he lived among us is not easy. Within a week there was talk about Borges, with Borges, because of Borges, and for Borges, in every corridor of Batts Hall. Scholars felt obliged to write studies and theses on Borges' work. Poets —wasn't it inevitable?—fired dithyrambic salvos at him.

I remember that, coinciding with Borges' arrival in Texas, some of us were reading his book *El hacedor*. Kim Taylor wanted to devote some pages of *The Texas Quarterly* to honoring the visiting Argentine writer. In them were included the first prose passages of *El hacedor* translated by Mildred Boyer and, among other pieces for and about Borges, poems by Harold Morland—translator of the verse in the present edition —and by Christopher Middleton. Borges was surrounded here with something that was more than enthusiasm—something I would almost call fervor. He was completely in his element, though he did at times long for Buenos Aires. Then he would ask us to take him to the banks of our little Colorado River; from there his imagination could carry him to the majestic estuary of the Plata. He especially enjoyed the company of Ramón Martínez-López, a philologist of incredible learning, who kept him company in endless etymological disquisitions, and Rudolph Willard, professor of Old and Middle English, who fed his most recent passion, the Anglo-Saxon epic.

Frank Wardlaw, partly in the line of duty, being director of a press pledged to the dissemination of Ibero-American literature in the United States, but also because he too caught our fever or fondness for Borges, asked the poet for permission to publish one of his books in English translation. And that is how the idea of this edition was born. Almost personal considerations, very human, very homey. For several months Borges was *our* poet and everyday friend. Professor Borges could not, in spite of himself and his vast knowledge, be the professor. The poet would get the better of him. If he sometimes caught himself speaking in a professorial tone, he would check himself, ever so subtly injecting a note of irony, or letting his imagination take flight so that we, his listeners, were imperceptibly led by the hand to the impossible and transparent realm that was his natural home.

With his consent to publish *El hacedor* in the United States, Borges gave his colleagues of The University of Texas the opportunity to transmit to the American reader something of the spirit of our friendly association with the most original of contemporary Spanish-American writers. From the very first pages the English-speaking reader will discover that this is an intimate, personal book. Very apt, therefore, to set up the same kind of simple but heart-felt relationship we fortunate Austinites enjoyed during some months. Borges considered *El hacedor*—I don't know whether he may have changed his mind—*his* book, the book most likely, in his opinion, to be remembered when all the rest are forgotten. And the book—Borges loved to play with this idea—that would make his earlier works unnecessary, including his two extraordinary collections of stories, *Ficciones* and *El Aleph.*[1] As is so often

[1] *Ficciones* has been translated into English in its entirety with Anthony Kerrigan as editor: *Ficciones*, New York, Grove Press, 1962. Part of this book, plus selected stories from *El Aleph* and *El hacedor*, have been published in English translation by James E. Irby (author of an excellent interpretive introduction to Borges' work) and Donald A. Yates in the volume entitled *Labyrinths. Selected Stories and Other Writings* (New York, New Directions, 1962).

the case, the reader, to say nothing of the critic, may not agree with the poet; they may well continue to think, and not without reason, that the great, the unique Borges is the Borges of narrative fiction. As for me, it is not my place to decide: I merely report what the artist felt and said.

For all of Borges' Texas friends this edition of *El hacedor* will also be a permanent memento of that great yet simple spirit who passed so briefly through our halls. Borges (if the critics will allow me) was largely right: read as it should be read, the present book contains—or insinuates, as we will shortly explain—all the poet wanted to tell us. We, his friends, old and new, accept it in that spirit, and are grateful.

Now, having set forth the personal considerations of the group of friends who contributed to the reality that is today this volume, I realize that there is something that I, individually, would like to add: perhaps a few lines, a sentence, a word—if there were one—that would be the living equivalent of one of the moments which Jorge Luis Borges' human presence filled on these Texas plains. But how can I express the accents of a voice grave and sweet, the flights of an extraordinary intelligence and imagination, the candor of a good and innocent soul, the quiet ache of a darkness and a loneliness we sensed, the magic of the poet who makes dreams come to life?

Many times I guided his uncertain steps through halls and down stairways, over the rough places of the island that is this out-of-the-way university. His poor sight allowed his friends the paradoxical task—misfortunate fortune—of guiding the best *seer* among modern poets in the Spanish language. To walk beside Borges, the great peripatetic conversationalist, was to enter and live in his world. The guide soon discovered, by the light that matters, that he himself was the blind one, and not the poet leaning on his arm.

El hacedor, the original version of which appeared in Buenos Aires in 1960, is to all appearances a miscellany. In it the author is supposed to have gathered odd poems, stories, parables, sketches, fragments, and apocryphal quotations, with no other purpose than to show what time accumulates in the bottom of a writer's desk drawer. But actually this juxtaposing of fragments, bits, and snippets corresponds to a poetic criterion of an extremely high order: that of creating a book—*the book*—which is the mirror of a life. A life in which, as Borges himself confesses, "few things have happened more worth remembering than Schopenhauer's thought or the music of England's words." A life that has been, more than anything else, an internal life, a truly private life of calm self-possession and "recogimiento."[2]

Borges has traveled a great deal. Sometimes he has made use of the customary media of transportation; but more often he has gone by way of his imagination. From his internal "recogimiento" he has ventured forth, on occasion, toward the strangest places and the remotest times. But his sallies have been only tentative explorations, amoebic assimilations of the external world. His work—and by now it can be viewed as a whole—is altogether poetic, personal, the work of a spirit so withdrawn that solitude has enlarged it and made him now see in that solitude the secret of the whole universe, now tremble before its undecipherable mysteries. Borges' "theme," then, throughout all his work—including his now famous fantasy narratives—has been simply Borges himself. It is true that, from all his excursions into nooks alien to his inner self —reading, travel, fleeting human relationships—Borges has come back burdened with every possible doubt except one. In spite of his intelligent, ironic, and painstaking defenses, each clash with external reality has reaffirmed his consciousness of self. With the world's reality in doubt, and man's, and even God's, only one certainty remains: that of being "somebody"—a particular individual, not very easily identifiable, for he could have been named Homer, Shakespeare, or, more modestly, Jorge Luis Borges—*creating himself* from within. This *hacedor*[3] is the creator, the poet, the man capable of

---

[2] There is no choice here but to use the untranslatable Spanish word, for to live in "recogimiento" is not simply to live in solitude; nor is it merely to live locked within oneself. A life of "recogimiento" is the life of the solitary man who accepts and lives in perfect harmony with his solitude, nurturing himself on what the soul has within it, an unfathomable and, for many, unsuspected treasure.

[3] In its original Spanish, the present book is called *El hacedor*, as is also the first narrative in the volume. This is perhaps the most symbolic and significant of the tales it contains. *Hacedor* means "maker" but it

"singing and leaving echoing concavely in the memory of man" murmurs—in prose and in verse—of Iliads, Odysseys, lost loves, obscure gestes, impossible and desperate adventures of fantasy. Security in this "somebody," this intimate self, is not based in Borges' case on a clear consciousness of his identity or personal destiny, but rather on the certainty of the compulsive, creative, poetic force that has borne him to the final stretch of his life work without faltering. The imprecise Homer-Borges of the story "El hacedor" knows very well that the weapon for combating life's final disillusionment, time's inexorable weight, and the terror and anguish of darkness, is none other than his capacity to dream and to sing. Dreams and song make the world bearable, habitable; they make the dark places bright. Blindness of the soul—which is the one that counts—is the natural state of man,[4] and woe to him who does not see in time that we live surrounded by shadows! The poet, the *hacedor*, makes this discovery one day and descends into the shadows unafraid, illumined by his creative consciousness. "In this night of his mortal eyes, into which he was now descending, love and danger were again waiting." Borges and Homer know, then, that this is where everything begins, in the bold, loving acceptance of life and in the drive that impels them to people their darkness with voices.

Dreams and song. About the whole and about the parts. About the universe and about each of its separate creatures. The creature may be a man—gaucho, hero, Irish patriot, impenitent Nazi, sacrificed Jew—any one of man's artifacts— a whole civilization, a library, a knife—or simply an animal, a tiger. "As I sleep, some dream beguiles me, and suddenly I know I am dreaming. Then I think: This is a dream, a pure diversion of my will; and now that I have unlimited power, I am going to cause a tiger."

But the *hacedor* must accept his ministry humbly.[5] He must

---

also has the meaning of creator. Thus God is spoken of as the "Supremo Hacedor."

[4] Borges is almost blind now. In the first story in this book the reader will immediately discover that the author identifies himself with the shade of Homer, who was also a blind poet and a seer-dreamer, one who peopled the world with echoes and murmurs that still resound.

[5] See "A Yellow Rose," in this volume: "Then the revelation occurred:

exercise his power, prepared, however, to recognize his ultimate impotence. For his office consists, precisely, in the will to
dream very high dreams and in attempting the purest, most
lasting resonances, all the while realizing and bravely accepting his incompetence. "Oh, incompetence! Never can my
dreams engender the wild beast I long for. The tiger indeed
appears, but stuffed or flimsy, or with impure variants of
shape, or of an implausible size, or all too fleeting, or with a
touch of the dog or the bird."

Dreams and song—in spite of incompetence, stumblings,
and disillusionment. This is why the *hacedor* and his book are
born. Their mission and message will not escape the reader
who knows when a dream is a dream and who has an ear for
remembering the melody of a song.

Let the reader not be confused. This book, though composed of
fragments, must be appraised as if it were a multiple mirror,
or a mosaic of tiny mirrors. At a certain distance from its
reading—once it has been digested—it will be clear that the
pieces outline a whole: a self-portrait of an entire soul and
body. The brilliant insinuation, the mysterious or ironic ref-
erence,[6] the small poetic incision, are Borges' chosen expres-
sive means. The story or short narrative, a form that made
him famous, and the novel—a genre he has avoided—always
seemed to him unpardonable excesses. That is why Borges
feels *El hacedor* is the culmination of a literary career, a
liberation from former limitations, vanities, and prejudices.
That is why he feels it is *his* book. How right he is, it is still
not time nor is this the place to judge; but the earnestness the
poet put into the effort ought to be clearly established. In
El hacedor stories, tales, and even poems are reduced to their
minimum, almost naked expression. Everything tends toward
the poetic parable: brief, but bright as a flash of lightning.

Since *El hacedor*, Borges has published an *Antología per-*

Marino *saw* the rose, as Adam might have seen it in Paradise, and he
sensed that the rose was to be found in its own eternity and not in his
words; and that we may mention or allude to a thing, but not express it."

[6] "Once I too sought expression; now I know my gods concede me only
allusion or mention of a thing" (Jorge Luis Borges, *Antología personal*
[Buenos Aires, Sur, 1961], p. 8).

sonal[7] in Argentina. In it he has collected, in preferential rather than chronological order, what to his mind can be submitted to the judgment of a hypothetical posterity. As the poet tells us in the prologue, the experiment has served only to prove to him his poverty, his limitations of expression, the mortality of his writings as measured by his rigorous criteria of today. But, at the same time, the task of anthologizing his own work has made him surer of himself, created a new source of vital energy, and given him a renewed illusion. "This poverty," says Borges "does not discourage me, since it gives me an illusion of continuity."

In my opinion, the several pieces that make up the present book, *El hacedor*, were also put together after Jorge Luis Borges had already begun to feel the pull of that anxiety for continuity. "For good or for ill, my readers"—Borges seems to be wanting to tell us in recent years—"these fragments piled up here by time are all that I am. The earlier work no longer matters." "The tall proud volumes casting a golden shadow in a corner were not—as his vanity had dreamed—a mirror of the world, but rather one thing more added *to* the world."[8] And this is all he as a poet feels capable of desiring: to be able to add to the world a few bits of more or less resplendent mirror yielding only an illusory reflection—ah, the timid yearning for immortality!—of what was felt, thought, and dreamed in solitude. The solitude, as we know, of one of the most solitary, intelligent, and sensitive souls of our time.

The poet is setting out, then, on his last venture. It makes one tremble to think with what assurance poets know when the final stage of a creative life begins; but at the same time it is wondrous to contemplate how the chaos that is their own life and work begins to take on meaning for them. Perhaps what is seen now will in retrospect be only another illusion, but there it is. When the uneven fragments that comprise the work are pieced together—especially the ones that appear most insignificant—they outline something the poet is consoled to behold. The parts organize themselves into a whole. "A man sets himself the task of portraying the world. Through

---

[7] Buenos Aires, Sur, 1961.
[8] See in detail the story "A Yellow Rose," in this edition.

the years he peoples a space with images of provinces, king-doms, mountains, bays, ships, islands, fishes, rooms, tools, stars, horses, and people. Shortly before his death, he discovers that that patient labyrinth of lines traces the image of his face."

If, after all, the face is merely the mirror of the soul, it is not hard to guess the ultimate meaning of the game of illusion Jorge Luis Borges proposes to the reader in this book: the separate parts that constitute *El hacedor*—narratives, poems, parables, reflections, and interpolations—when read as a whole, trace the image of the poet's face: face-mirror-image of the soul of the creator, of the maker.

At first glance, there is nothing unusual about one poet's dedicating one of his books to another poet. That *El hacedor* should be dedicated to Leopoldo Lugones[9] is something that need not be mentioned in this introduction if it were not that the explanation Borges gives for his dedication at the begin-ning of the volume requires a special imaginative effort on the part of the reader. Actually, without such an effort one can-not wholly enter the mysterious realm where the poet lives his dreams. The invocation of the shade of Lugones—who committed suicide in 1938—on the threshold of *El hacedor* is revealing. It is an exorcism.

The dream and the song of *El hacedor* are troubled from the start by old, malignant spirits. In conjuring his former de-mons—passion, intellectual pride, rebellion against the voice of the once omnipresent poet—Borges wants to be done with them. It is not merely a question of appeasing the memory of the Modernist poet, against whom Borges and his young friends in 1921 launched the most violent attacks and obstrep-erous jibes. Nor of recognizing, out of the creative maturity of his sixties, the right and dignity of literary prestige honor-ably won. Borges intends to do this, of course, but much more as well. He wants now to incorporate into his book, into his

[9] Leopoldo Lugones (1874–1938) is the most famous of the Argentine Modernist poets. He was born in a provincial town in Córdoba and took his own life with cyanide in 1938, in Tigre, near Buenos Aires. Lugones was the most important renovating force in Argentine poetry and prose in the twentieth century. His best-known works are *Las montañas del oro* (1897), *Los crepúsculos del jardín* (1905), *Las fuerzas extrañas* (1906), *Lunario sentimental* (1909), and *La guerra gaucha* (1911).

song, the feeling that in his hostility toward the great poet of the generation preceding his own there was somehow a great and heartfelt love. For without internal peace and order the poet cannot truly face the chaos of life, or manage to have his work's labyrinth of lines trace the image of his face.

There is, besides, a certain fascination in his recollection of Lugones. Borges is the present director of the National Library in Buenos Aires; in 1938, Lugones was director of the Library of the National Council of Education. In his dedication Borges deliberately fuses and confuses the two libraries and the two times, past and present: "Leaving behind the babble of the plaza, I enter the Library. I feel, almost physically, the magnetic force of the books, an ambient serenity of order, time magically desiccated and preserved." The intent is quite clear: "My vanity and nostalgia have set up an impossible scene," says Borges. The impossibility is not merely physical; it depends rather on the fact that it is a wish, a dream, too distant to be attainable; for what the poet dreams of is nothing less than a loving communion between the voices of the poets. "Perhaps so," says Borges to himself in his illusions, "but tomorrow I too will have died and our times will intermingle and chronology will be lost in a sphere of symbols. And then in some way it will be right to claim that I have brought you this book and that you, Lugones, have accepted it."

From the very first pages, therefore, the reader can discover where the poet is going in the rest of the book. Besides, without the initial exorcism of the demons of frivolity, routine reading, and pedantry, the reader might even be prevented from coming at last to trace out the portrait of his own face. And to reach this moment to which every reader—a passive poet—should be led by the hand of the *hacedor*, the active poet, there is no other way than to exorcise oneself and make ready to dream and to hear the murmurs that are heard in dreams.

Miguel Enguídanos
Austin, June 1963

PART ONE

Translated by Mildred Boyer

To Leopoldo Lugones

Leaving behind the babble of the plaza, I enter the Library. I feel, almost physically, the gravitation of the books, the enveloping serenity of order, time magically desiccated and preserved. Left and right, absorbed in their shining dreams, the readers' momentary profiles are sketched by the light of their bright officious lamps, to use Milton's hypallage. I remember having remembered that figure before in this place, and afterwards that other epithet that also defines these environs, the "arid camel" of the Lunario, *and then that hexameter from the* Aeneid *that uses the same artifice and surpasses artifice itself:* Ibant obscuri sola sub nocte per umbras.

These reflections bring me to the door of your office. I go in; we exchange a few words, conventional and cordial, and I give you this book. If I am not mistaken, you were not disinclined to me, Lugones, and you would have liked to like some piece of my work. That never happened; but this time you turn the pages and read approvingly a verse here and there— perhaps because you have recognized your own voice in it, perhaps because deficient practice concerns you less than solid theory.

At this point my dream dissolves, like water in water. The vast library that surrounds me is on Mexico Street, not on Rodríguez Peña, and you, Lugones, killed yourself early in '38. My vanity and nostalgia have set up an impossible scene. Perhaps so (I tell myself), but tomorrow I too will have died, and our times will intermingle and chronology will be lost in a sphere of symbols. And then in some way it will be right to claim that I have brought you this book, and that you have accepted it.

J. L. B.

Buenos Aires, August 9, 1960

The Maker

He had never dwelled on memory's delights. Impressions slid over him, vivid but ephemeral. A potter's vermilion; the heavens laden with stars that were also gods; the moon, from which a lion had fallen; the slick feel of marble beneath slow sensitive fingertips; the taste of wild boar meat, eagerly torn by his white teeth; a Phoenician word; the black shadow a lance casts on yellow sand; the nearness of the sea or of a woman; a heavy wine, its roughness cut by honey—these could fill his soul completely. He knew what terror was, but he also knew anger and rage, and once he had been the first to scale an enemy wall. Eager, curious, casual, with no other law than fulfillment and the immediate indifference that ensues, he walked the varied earth and saw, on one seashore or another, the cities of men and their palaces. In crowded marketplaces or at the foot of a mountain whose uncertain peak might be inhabited by satyrs, he had listened to complicated tales which he accepted, as he accepted reality, without asking whether they were true or false.

Gradually now the beautiful universe was slipping away from him. A stubborn mist erased the outline of his hand, the night was no longer peopled by stars, the earth beneath his feet was unsure. Everything was growing distant and blurred. When he knew he was going blind he cried out; stoic modesty had not yet been invented and Hector could flee with impunity. I will not see again, he felt, either the sky filled with mythical dread, or this face that the years will transform. Over this desperation of his flesh passed days and nights. But one morning he awoke; he looked, no longer alarmed, at the dim things that surrounded him; and inexplicably he sensed, as one recognizes a tune or a voice, that now it was over and that he had faced it, with fear but also with joy, hope, and curiosity. Then he descended into his memory, which seemed to him endless, and up from that vertigo he succeeded in bringing forth a forgotten recollection that shone like a coin under the rain, perhaps because he had never looked at it, unless in a dream.

The recollection was like this. Another boy had insulted him and he had run to his father and told him about it. His father let him talk as if he were not listening or did not understand; and he took down from the wall a bronze dagger, beautiful and charged with power, which the boy had secretly coveted. Now he had it in his hands and the surprise of possession obliterated the affront he had suffered. But his father's voice was saying, "Let someone know you are a man," and there was a command in his voice. The night blotted out the paths; clutching the dagger, in which he felt the foreboding of a magic power, he descended the rough hillside that surrounded the house and ran to the seashore, dreaming he was Ajax and Perseus and peopling the salty darkness with battles and wounds. The exact taste of that moment was what he was seeking now; the rest did not matter: the insults of the duel, the rude combat, the return home with the bloody blade.

Another memory, in which there was also a night and an imminence of adventure, sprang out of that one. A woman, the first the gods set aside for him, had waited for him in the shadow of a hypogeum, and he had searched for her through corridors that were like stone nets, along slopes that sank into the shadow. Why did those memories come back to him, and why did they come without bitterness, as a mere foreshadowing of the present?

In grave amazement he understood. In this night too, in this night of his mortal eyes into which he was now descending, love and danger were again waiting. Ares and Aphrodite, for already he divined (already it encircled him) a murmur of glory and hexameters, a murmur of men defending a temple the gods will not save, and of black vessels searching the sea for a beloved isle, the murmur of the Odysseys and Iliads it was his destiny to sing and leave echoing concavely in the memory of man. These things we know, but not those that he felt when he descended into the last shade of all.

Dreamtigers

In my childhood I was a fervent worshiper of the tiger: not the jaguar, the spotted "tiger" of the Amazonian tangles and the isles of vegetation that float down the Paraná, but that striped, Asiatic, royal tiger, that can be faced only by a man of war, on a castle atop an elephant. I used to linger endlessly before one of the cages at the zoo; I judged vast encyclopedias and books of natural history by the splendor of their tigers. (I still remember those illustrations: I who cannot rightly recall the brow or the smile of a woman.) Childhood passed away, and the tigers and my passion for them grew old, but still they are in my dreams. At that submerged or chaotic level they keep prevailing. And so, as I sleep, some dream beguiles me, and suddenly I know I am dreaming. Then I think: This is a dream, a pure diversion of my will; and now that I have unlimited power, I am going to cause a tiger.

Oh, incompetence! Never can my dreams engender the wild beast I long for. The tiger indeed appears, but stuffed or flimsy, or with impure variations of shape, or of an implausible size, or all too fleeting, or with a touch of the dog or the bird.

A : "Absorbed in rationalizing about immortality, we had let
dusk come without lighting the lamp. We could not see each
other's faces. He kept repeating that the soul is immortal, and
the indifference and sweetness of Macedonio Fernández's voice
were more convincing than fervor ever could have been. He
was assuring me that the death of the body is entirely insignificant and that dying must perforce be the fact most null
and void that can happen to a man. I sat playing with Macedonio's clasp knife, opening and closing it. A nearby accordion
kept infinitely grinding out *La Cumparsita,* that worn-out
trifle loved by so many because they think it's old—I proposed
that Macedonio and I commit suicide so we could go on dis-
cussing without being bothered."

Z : (*joking*): "But I suspect that in the end you decided not
to do it."

A : (*now fully mystical*): "I don't really recall whether we
committed suicide that night."

Toenails

Soft stockings coddle them by day and nail-bossed leather
shoes buttress them, but my toes refuse to pay attention. Nothing interests them but emitting toenails, horny plates, semi-
transparent and elastic, to defend themselves—from whom?
Stupid and mistrustful as they alone can be, they never for a
moment stop readying that tenuous armament. They reject
the universe and its ecstasy to keep forever elaborating useless
sharp ends, which rude Solingen scissors snip over and over
again. Ninety days along in the dawn of prenatal confinement,
they established that singular industry. When I am laid away,
in an ash-colored house provided with dead flowers and amu-
lets, they will still go on with their stubborn task, until they
are moderated by decay. They—and the beard on my face.

The Draped Mirrors

Islam asserts that on the unappealable day of judgment every perpetrator of the image of a living creature will be raised from the dead with his works, and he will be commanded to bring them to life, and he will fail, and be cast out with them into the fires of punishment. As a child, I felt before large mirrors that same horror of a spectral duplication or multiplication of reality. Their infallible and continuous functioning, their pursuit of my actions, their cosmic pantomime, were uncanny then, whenever it began to grow dark. One of my persistent prayers to God and my guardian angel was that I not dream about mirrors. I know I watched them with misgivings. Sometimes I feared they might begin to deviate from reality; other times I was afraid of seeing there my own face, disfigured by strange calamities. I have learned that this fear is again monstrously abroad in the world. The story is simple indeed, and disagreeable.

Around 1927 I met a sombre girl, first by telephone (for Julia began as a nameless, faceless voice), and, later, on a corner toward evening. She had alarmingly large eyes, straight blue-black hair, and an unbending body. Her grandfather and great-grandfather were *federales*, as mine were *unitarios*, and that ancient discord in our blood was for us a bond, a fuller possession of the fatherland. She lived with her family in a big old run-down house with very high ceilings, in the vapidity and grudges of genteel poverty. Afternoons—some few times in the evening—we went strolling in her neighborhood, Balvanera. We followed the thick wall by the railroad; once we walked along Sarmiento as far as the clearing for the Parque Centenario. There was no love between us, or even pretense of love: I sensed in her an intensity that was altogether foreign to the erotic, and I feared it. It is not uncommon to relate to women, in an urge for intimacy, true or apochryphal circumstances of one's boyish past. I must have told her once about the mirrors and thus in 1928 I prompted a hallucination that was to flower in 1931. Now, I have just learned that she has lost her mind and that the mirrors in her room are draped because she sees in them my reflection, usurping her own, and she trembles and falls silent and says I am persecuting her by magic.

What bitter slavishness, that of my face, that of one of my former faces. This odious fate reserved for my features must perforce make me odious too, but I no longer care.

Argumentum Ornithologicum

I close my eyes and see a flock of birds. The vision lasts a second or perhaps less; I don't know how many birds I saw. Were they a definite or an indefinite number? This problem involves the question of the existence of God. If God exists, the number is definite, because how many birds I saw is known to God. If God does not exist, the number is indefinite, because nobody was able to take count. In this case, I saw fewer than ten birds (let's say) and more than one; but I did not see nine, eight, seven, six, five, four, three, or two birds. I saw a number between ten and one, but not nine, eight, seven, six, five, etc. That number, as a whole number, is inconceivable; *ergo*, God exists.

The Captive

The story is told in Junín or in Tapalqué. A boy disappeared after an Indian attack. People said the Indians had kidnaped him. His parents searched for him in vain. Then, long years later, a soldier who came from the interior told them about an Indian with blue eyes who might well be their son. At length they found him (the chronicle has lost the circumstances and I will not invent what I do not know) and thought they recognized him. The man, buffeted by the wilderness and the barbaric life, no longer knew how to understand the words of his mother tongue, but indifferent and docile, he let himself be led home. There he stopped, perhaps because the others stopped. He looked at the door as if he did not know what it was for. Then suddenly he lowered his head, let out a shout, ran across the entrance way and the two long patios, and plunged into the kitchen. Without hesitating, he sank his arm into the blackened chimney and pulled out the little horn-handled knife he had hidden there as a boy. His eyes shone with joy and his parents wept because they had found their son.

Perhaps this recollection was followed by others, but the Indian could not live within walls, and one day he went in search of his wilderness. I wonder what he felt in that dizzying moment when past and present became one. I wonder whether the lost son was reborn and died in that instant of ecstasy; and whether he ever managed to recognize, if only as an infant or a dog does, his parents and his home.

The Sham

It was one day in July, 1952, when the mourner appeared in that little town in the Chaco. He was tall, thin, Indian-like, with the inexpressive face of a mask or a dullard. People treated him with deference, not for himself but rather for the person he represented or had already become. He chose a site near the river. With the help of some local women he set up a board on two wooden horses and on top a cardboard box with a blond doll in it. In addition, they lit four candles in tall candlesticks and put flowers around. People were not long in coming. Hopeless old women, gaping children, peasants whose cork helmets were respectfully removed, filed past the box and repeated, "Deepest sympathy, General." He, very sorrowful, received them at the head of the box, his hands crossed over his stomach in the attitude of a pregnant woman. He held out his right hand to shake the hands they extended to him and replied with dignity and resignation: "It was fate. Everything humanly possible was done." A tin money box received the two-peso fee, and many came more than once.

What kind of man, I ask myself, conceived and executed that funereal farce? A fanatic, a pitiful wretch, a victim of hallucinations, or an impostor and a cynic? Did he believe he was Perón as he played his suffering role as the macabre widower? The story is incredible, but it happened, and perhaps not once but many times, with different actors in different locales. It contains the perfect cipher of an unreal epoch; it is like the reflection of a dream or like that drama-within-the-drama we see in *Hamlet*. The mourner was not Perón and the blond doll was not the woman Eva Duarte, but neither was Perón Perón, nor was Eva Eva. They were, rather, unknown individuals—or anonymous ones whose secret names and true faces we do not know—who acted out, for the credulous love of the lower middle classes, a crass mythology.

We said goodbye at the corner of Eleventh. From the other sidewalk I turned to look back; you too had turned, and you waved goodbye to me.

A river of vehicles and people were flowing between us. It was five o'clock on an ordinary afternoon. How was I to know that that river was Acheron the doleful, the insuperable?

We did not see each other again, and a year later you were dead.

And now I seek out that memory and look at it, and I think it was false, and that behind that trivial farewell was infinite separation.

Last night I stayed in after dinner and reread, in order to understand these things, the last teaching Plato put in his master's mouth. I read that the soul may escape when the flesh dies.

And now I do not know whether the truth is in the ominous subsequent interpretation, or in the unsuspecting farewell.

For if souls do not die, it is right that we should not make much of saying goodbye.

To say goodbye to each other is to deny separation. It is like saying "today we play at separating, but we will see each other tomorrow." Man invented farewells because he somehow knows he is immortal, even though he may seem gratuitous and ephemeral.

Sometime, Delia, we will take up again—beside what river? —this uncertain dialogue, and we will ask each other if ever, in a city lost on a plain, we were Borges and Delia.

He arrived from southern England early one winter morning in 1877. Ruddy, athletic, and obese as he was, almost everyone inevitably thought he was English, and to tell the truth he was remarkably like the archetypical John Bull. He wore a top hat and a strange wool cape with an opening in the middle. A group of men, women, and children anxiously waited for him. Many had their throats marked with a red line; others were headless and moved uncertainly, like a man walking in the dark. Little by little they surrounded the stranger, and out of the crowd someone shouted an ugly word, but an ancient terror stopped them at that. Then a military man with a yellowish skin and eyes like firebrands stepped forward. His disheveled hair and murky beard seemed to gobble up his face. Ten or twelve mortal wounds furrowed his body like the stripes on a tiger's skin. The stranger, seeing him, changed color suddenly; then he advanced and stretched out his hand.

"How it grieves me to see such an honorable warrior struck down by the arms of treachery!" he said roundly. "But what an intimate satisfaction, too, to have ordered that the acolytes who attended the sacrifice should purge their deeds on the scaffold in Victoria Square!"

"If you are speaking of Santos Pérez and the Reinafés, I would like you to know I have already thanked them," said the bloody one with measured gravity.

The other man looked at him as if he suspected him of joking or of making a threat, but Quiroga went on:

"Rosas, you never did understand me. And how could you, when our destinies were so different? Your lot was to command in a city that looks toward Europe and will someday be among the most famous in the world. Mine was to wage war in America's lonely spots, on poor earth belonging to poor gauchos. My empire was made of lances and shouts and sand pits and almost secret victories in obscure places. What claims are those to fame? I live and will continue to live for many years in the people's memory because I was murdered in a stagecoach at a place called Barranca Yaco, by horsemen armed with swords. It is you I have to thank for this gift of a bizarre death, which I did not know how to appreciate then, but which subsequent generations have refused to forget. You undoubtedly know of some exquisite lithographs, and the interesting book edited by a worthy citizen of San Juan."

Rosas, who had recovered his aplomb, looked at him disdainfully.

"You are a romantic," he pronounced. "The flattery of posterity is not worth much more than contemporary flattery, which is worth nothing, and can be had on the strength of a few medals."

"I know your way of thinking," answered Quiroga. "In 1852, destiny, either out of generosity or out of a desire to sound you to your depths, offered you a real man's death in battle. You showed yourself unworthy of that gift: the blood and fighting scared you."

"Scared?" repeated Rosas. "Me, who busted broncs in the South, and later busted a whole country?"

For the first time Quiroga smiled.

"I know," he said slowly, "that you have cut more than one fine figure on horseback, according to the impartial testimony of your foremen and hands; but other fine figures were cut in America in those days, and they were also on horseback—figures called Chacabuco and Junín and Palma Redonda and Caseros."

Rosas listened without changing expression and replied:

"I did not have to be brave. One 'fine figure' of mine, as you call it, was to manage that braver men than I should fight and die for me. Santos Pérez, for example, who finished you off. Bravery is a question of holding out; some can hold out more than others, but sooner or later they all give in."

"That may be true," said Quiroga, "but I have lived and died and to this day I do not know what fear is. And now I am going to be obliterated, to be given another face and another destiny, for history has had its fill of violent men. Who the other one will be, what they will make of me, I do not know; but I know he will not be afraid.

"I am satisfied to be who I am," said Rosas, "and I want to be no one else."

"The stones want to be stones forever, too," said Quiroga, "and for centuries they are, until they crumble into dust. I

34

thought as you do when I entered death, but I learned many things here. Just look, we are both changing already."

But Rosas paid no attention and said, as if thinking aloud:

"It must be that I am not made to be a dead man, but these places and this discussion seem like a dream, and not a dream dreamed by me but by someone else still to be born."

They spoke no more, for at that moment Someone called them.

To make his horror complete, Caesar, pressed to the foot of a statue by the impatient daggers of his friends, discovers among the blades and faces the face of Marcus Junius Brutus, his protégé, perhaps his son, and ceasing to defend himself he exclaims: "You too, my son!" Shakespeare and Quevedo revive the pathetic cry.

Destiny takes pleasure in repetition, variants, symmetries: nineteen centuries later, in the south of the Province of Buenos Aires, a gaucho is attacked by other gauchos. As he falls he recognizes an adopted son of his and says to him with gentle reproof and slow surprise (these words must be heard, not read), "Pero che!" He is being killed, and he does not know he is dying so that a scene may be repeated.

A Problem

Let us imagine that in Toledo someone finds a paper with an Arabic text and that the paleographers declare the handwriting belongs to that same Cide Hamete Benengeli from whom Cervantes took his Don Quixote. In the text we read that the hero—who, the story goes, rambled about Spain armed with a sword and a lance, challenging all sorts of people for all sorts of reasons—discovers at the end of one of his many frays that he has killed a man. At this point the fragment breaks off. The problem is to guess, or to conjecture, how Don Quixote reacts.

As I see it, there are three possible solutions. The first is negative. Nothing special happens, for in the hallucinatory world of Don Quixote death is no less common than magic, and to have killed a man need not perturb someone who struggles, or thinks he struggles, with monsters and enchanters. The second is pathetic. Don Quixote never managed to forget that he was a projection of Alonso Quijano, a reader of fairy tales. Seeing death, realizing that a dream has led him to commit the sin of Cain, wakes him from his pampered madness, possibly forever. The third is perhaps the most plausible. Having killed the man, Don Quixote cannot admit that his terrible act is the fruit of a delirium. The reality of the effect forces him to presuppose a parallel reality of the cause, and Don Quixote will never emerge from his madness.

There remains another conjecture, alien to the Spanish world and even to the Occidental world. It requires a much more ancient setting, more complex, and wearier. Don Quixote, who is no longer Don Quixote but rather a king of the Hindustani cycles, intuitively knows as he stands before his enemy's cadaver that to kill and to beget are divine or magical acts which manifestly transcend humanity. He knows that the dead man is an illusion, as is the bloody sword that weighs down his hand, as is he himself, and all his past life, and the vast gods, and the universe.

Neither that afternoon nor the next did the illustrious Giam-
battista Marino die, he whom the unanimous mouths of Fame
—to use an image dear to him—proclaimed as the new Homer
and the new Dante. But the still, noiseless fact that took place
then was in reality the last event of his life. Laden with years
and with glory, he lay dying on a huge Spanish bed with
carved bedposts. It is not hard to imagine a serene balcony a
few steps away, facing the west, and, below, marble and
laurels and a garden whose various levels are duplicated in a
rectangle of water. A woman has placed in a goblet a yellow
rose. The man murmurs the inevitable lines that now, to tell
the truth, bore even him a little:

> Purple of the garden, pomp of the meadow,
> Gem of spring, April's eye . . .

Then the revelation occurred: Marino saw the rose as Adam
might have seen it in Paradise, and he thought that the rose
was to be found in its own eternity and not in his words; and
that we may mention or allude to a thing, but not express it;
and that the tall, proud volumes casting a golden shadow in a
corner were not—as his vanity had dreamed—a mirror of the
world, but rather one thing more added to the world.

Marino achieved this illumination on the eve of his death,
and Homer and Dante may have achieved it as well.

The Witness

In a stable that stands almost within the shadow of the new stone church a gray-eyed, gray-bearded man, stretched out amid the odor of the animals, humbly seeks death as one seeks for sleep. The day, faithful to vast secret laws, little by little shifts and mingles the shadows in the humble nook. Outside are the plowed fields and a deep ditch clogged with dead leaves and an occasional wolf track in the black earth at the edge of the forest. The man sleeps and dreams, forgotten. The angelus awakens him. By now the sound of the bells is one of the habits of evening in the kingdoms of England. But this man, as a child, saw the face of Woden, the holy dread and exultation, the rude wooden idol weighed down with Roman coins and heavy vestments, the sacrifice of horses, dogs, and prisoners. Before dawn he will die, and in him will die, never to return, the last eye-witness of those pagan rites; the world will be a little poorer when this Saxon dies.

Events far-reaching enough to people all space, whose end is nonetheless tolled when one man dies, may cause us wonder. But something, or an infinite number of things, dies in every death, unless the universe is possessed of a memory, as the theosophists have supposed.

In the course of time there was a day that closed the last eyes to see Christ. The battle of Junín and the love of Helen each died with the death of some one man. What will die with me when I die, what pitiful or perishable form will the world lose? The voice of Macedonio Fernández? The image of a roan horse on the vacant lot at Serrano and Charcas? A bar of sulphur in the drawer of a mahogany desk?

Out of this city marched armies that seemed to be great, and afterwards were, when glory had magnified them. As the years went by, an occasional soldier returned and, with a foreign trace in his speech, told tales of what had happened to him in places called Ituzaingó or Ayacucho. These things, now, are as if they had never been.

Two tyrannies had their day here. During the first some men coming from the Plata market hawked white and yellow peaches from the seat of a cart. A child lifted a corner of the canvas that covered them and saw *unitario* heads with bloody beards. The second, for many, meant imprisonment and death; for all it meant discomfort, a taste of disgrace in everyday acts, an incessant humiliation. These things, now, are as if they had never been.

A man who knew all words looked with minute love at the plants and birds of this land and described them, perhaps forever, and wrote in metaphors of metal the vast chronicle of the tumultuous sunsets and the shapes of the moon. These things, now, are as if they had never been.

Here too the generations have known those common and somehow eternal vicissitudes which are the stuff of art. These things, now, are as if they had never been. But in a hotel room in the 1860's, or thereabouts, a man dreamed about a fight. A gaucho lifts a Negro off his feet with his knife, throws him down like a sack of bones, sees him agonize and die, crouches down to clean his blade, unties his horse, and mounts slowly so he will not be thought to be running away. This, which once was, is again infinitely: the splendid armies are gone, and a lowly knife fight remains. The dream of one man is part of the memory of all.

I saw in a hall an arrow pointing the way and I thought that this inoffensive symbol had once been a thing of iron, an inescapable and fatal projectile that pierced the flesh of men and of lions and clouded the sun at Thermopylae and gave Harald Sigurdarson six feet of English earth forever.

Some days later someone showed me a photograph of a Magyar horseman. A coiled lasso circled the breast of his mount. I learned that the lasso, which once whipped through the air and brought down the bulls of the prairie, was now nothing more than a haughty trapping of Sunday harness.

In the west cemetery I saw a runic cross, chiseled in red marble. The arms curved as they widened out, and a circle encompassed them. That limited, circumscribed cross represented the other one, the free-armed cross, which in its turn represents the gallows where a god suffered, the "vile machine" railed at by Lucian of Samosata.

Cross, lasso, and arrow—former tools of man, debased or exalted now to the status of symbols. Why should I marvel at them, when there is not a single thing on earth that oblivion does not erase or memory change, and when no one knows into what images he himself will be transmuted by the future.

Weary of his land of Spain, an old soldier of the king sought solace in Ariosto's vast geographies, in that valley of the moon where misspent dream-time goes, and in the golden idol of Mohammed stolen by Montalbán.

In gentle mockery of himself he conceived a credulous man who, unsettled by the marvels he read about, hit upon the idea of seeking noble deeds and enchantments in prosaic places called El Toboso or Montiel.

Defeated by reality, by Spain, Don Quixote died in his native village around 1614. He was survived only briefly by Miguel de Cervantes.

For both of them, for the dreamer and the dreamed, the tissue of that whole plot consisted in the contraposition of two worlds: the unreal world of the books of chivalry and the common everyday world of the seventeenth century.

Little did they suspect that the years would end by wearing away the disharmony. Little did they suspect that La Mancha and Montiel and the knight's frail figure would be, for the future, no less poetic than Sindbad's haunts or Ariosto's vast geographies.

For myth is at the beginning of literature, and also at its end.

Devoto Clinic, January 1955.

Diodorus Siculus tells the story of a god, broken and scattered abroad. What man of us has never felt, walking through the twilight or writing down a date from his past, that he has lost something infinite?

Mankind has lost a face, an irretrievable face, and all have longed to be that pilgrim—imagined in the Empyrean, beneath the Rose—who in Rome sees the Veronica and murmurs in faith, "Lord Jesus, my God, true God, is this then what Thy face was like?"

Beside a road there is a stone face and an inscription that says, "The True Portrait of the Holy Face of the God of Jaén." If we truly knew what it was like, the key to the parables would be ours and we would know whether the son of the carpenter was also the Son of God.

Paul saw it as a light that struck him to the ground; John, as the sun when it shines in all its strength; Teresa de Jesús saw it many times, bathed in tranquil light, yet she was never sure of the color of His eyes.

We lost those features, as one may lose a magic number made up of the usual ciphers, as one loses an image in a kaleidoscope, forever. We may see them and know them not. The profile of a Jew in the subway is perhaps the profile of Christ; perhaps the hands that give us our change at a ticket window duplicate the ones some soldiers nailed one day to the cross.

Perhaps a feature of the crucified face lurks in every mirror; perhaps the face died, was erased, so that God may be all of us.

Who knows but that tonight we may see it in the labyrinth of dreams, and tomorrow not know we saw it.

Parable of the Palace

That day, the Yellow Emperor showed the poet his palace. They left behind, in long succession, the first terraces on the west which descend, like the steps of an almost measureless amphitheater, to a paradise or garden whose metal mirrors and intricate juniper hedges already prefigured the labyrinth. They lost themselves in it, gaily at first, as if condescending to play a game, but afterwards not without misgiving, for its straight avenues were subject to a curvature, ever so slight, but continuous (and secretly those avenues were circles). Toward midnight observation of the planets and the opportune sacrifice of a turtle permitted them to extricate themselves from that seemingly bewitched region, but not from the sense of being lost, for this accompanied them to the end. Foyers and patios and libraries they traversed then, and a hexagonal room with a clepsydra, and one morning from a tower they descried a stone man, whom they then lost sight of forever. Many shining rivers did they cross in sandalwood canoes, or a single river many times. The imperial retinue would pass and people would prostrate themselves. But one day they put in on an island where someone did not do it, because he had never seen the Son of Heaven, and the executioner had to decapitate him. Black heads of hair and black dances and complicated golden masks did their eyes indifferently behold; the real and the dreamed became one, or rather reality was one of dream's configurations. It seemed impossible that earth were anything but gardens, pools, architectures, and splendrous forms. Every hundred paces a tower cleft the air; to the eye their color was identical, yet the first of all was yellow, and the last, scarlet, so delicate were the gradations and so long the series.

It was at the foot of the next-to-the-last tower that the poet —who was as if untouched by the wonders that amazed the rest—recited the brief composition we find today indissolubly linked to his name and which, as the more elegant historians have it, gave him immortality and death. The text has been lost. There are some who contend it consisted of a single line; others say it had but a single word. The truth, the incredible truth, is that in the poem stood the enormous palace, entire and minutely detailed, with each illustrious porcelain and every sketch on every porcelain and the shadows and the light of the twilights and each unhappy or joyous moment of the glorious dynasties of mortals, gods, and dragons who had dwelled in it from the interminable past. All fell silent, but the Emperor exclaimed, "You have robbed me of my palace!" And the executioner's iron sword cut the poet down.

Others tell the story differently. There cannot be any two things alike in the world; the poet, they say, had only to utter the poem to make the palace disappear, as if abolished and blown to bits by the final syllable. Such legends, of course, amount to no more than literary fiction. The poet was a slave of the Emperor and as such he died. His composition sank into oblivion because it deserved oblivion and his descendants still seek, nor will they find, the one word that contains the universe.

There was no one in him; behind his face (which even in the poor paintings of the period is unlike any other) and his words, which were copious, imaginative, and emotional, there was nothing but a little chill, a dream not dreamed by anyone. At first he thought everyone was like him, but the puzzled look on a friend's face when he remarked on that emptiness told him he was mistaken and convinced him forever that an individual must not differ from his species. Occasionally he thought he would find in books the cure for his ill, and so he learned the small Latin and less Greek of which a contemporary was to speak. Later he thought that in the exercise of an elemental human rite he might well find what he sought, and he let himself be initiated by Anne Hathaway one long June afternoon. At twenty-odd he went to London. Instinctively, he had already trained himself in the habit of pretending that he was someone, so it would not be discovered that he was no one. In London he hit upon the profession to which he was predestined, that of the actor, who plays on stage at being someone else. His playacting taught him a singular happiness, perhaps the first he had known; but when the last line was applauded and the last corpse removed from the stage, the hated sense of unreality came over him again. He ceased to be Ferrex or Tamburlaine and again became a nobody. Trapped, he fell to imagining other heroes and other tragic tales. Thus, while in London's bawdyhouses and taverns his body fulfilled its destiny as body, the soul that dwelled in it was Caesar, failing to heed the augurer's admonition, and Juliet, detesting the lark, and Macbeth, conversing on the heath with the witches, who are also the fates. Nobody was ever as many men as that man, who like the Egyptian Proteus managed to exhaust all the possible shapes of being. At times he slipped into some corner of his work a confession, certain that it would not be deciphered; Richard affirms that in his single person he plays many parts, and Iago says with strange words, "I am not what I am." His passages on the fundamental identity of existing, dreaming, and acting are famous.

Twenty years he persisted in that controlled hallucination,

but one morning he was overcome by the surfeit and the horror of being so many kings who die by the sword and so many unhappy lovers who converge, diverge, and melodiously agonize. That same day he disposed of his theater. Before a week was out he had returned to the village of his birth, where he recovered the trees and the river of his childhood; and he did not bind them to those others his muse had celebrated, those made illustrious by mythological allusions and Latin phrases. He had to be someone; he became a retired impresario who has made his fortune and who interests himself in loans, lawsuits, and petty usury. In this character he dictated the arid final will and testament that we know, deliberately excluding from it every trace of emotion and of literature. Friends from London used to visit his retreat, and for them he would take on again the role of poet.

The story goes that, before or after he died, he found himself before God and he said: "I, who have been so many men in vain, want to be one man: myself." The voice of God replied from a whirlwind: "Neither am I one self; I dreamed the world as you dreamed your work, my Shakespeare, and among the shapes of my dream are you, who, like me, are many persons—and none."

In dreams, writes Coleridge, images represent the sensations we think they cause: we do not feel horror because we are threatened by a sphinx; we dream of a sphinx in order to explain the horror we feel. If this is so, how could a mere chronicle of the shapes that that night's dream took communicate the bewilderment, the exaltation, the alarm, the menace, and the jubilation that wove it together? None the less, I shall attempt that chronicle. Perhaps the fact that a single scene united the dream will remove or alleviate the essential difficulty.

The scene was the College of Philosophy and Letters, the hour twilight. As usual in dreams, everything was a little different; a slight enlargement altered things. We were electing officers. I was talking with Pedro Henríquez Ureña, who in the waking world has been dead for many years. Suddenly we were interrupted by a clamor as of a demonstration or a band of street musicians. Howls, both animal and human, rose from Below. A voice cried out, "Here they come!" and then, "The Gods! The Gods!" Four or five fellows emerged from the mob and took over the platform of the assembly hall. We all applauded, weeping: these were the Gods, returning after a centuries-long exile. Exalted by the platform, their heads thrown back and their chests out, they haughtily received our homage. One was holding a branch which conformed, no doubt, to the simple botany of dreams; another, in a broad gesture, held out his hand—a claw; one of the faces of Janus looked suspiciously at the curved beak of Thoth. Goaded perhaps by our applause, one, I do not know which, broke out in a victorious and incredibly bitter cackle, half gargle, half whistle. From that moment on, things changed.

It all began with the suspicion, perhaps exaggerated, that the Gods could not talk. Centuries of brutish and bloodthirsty life had atrophied whatever there had been of the human in them. Islam's moon and Rome's cross had dealt implacably with those fugitives. Low foreheads, yellow teeth, sparse mustaches like a mulatto's or a Chinaman's, and thick bestial lips bespoke the degeneration of the Olympian lineage. Their garments were less suited to decorous, decent poverty than to the evil sumptuousness of the gambling dens and bawdy houses of Below. In the buttonhole of one bled a red carnation; beneath the tight-fitting jacket of another bulged the form of a dagger. Suddenly we felt they were playing their last card, that they were crafty, ignorant, and cruel as old beasts of prey, and that if we allowed ourselves to be won over by fear or pity, they would end by destroying us.

We drew our heavy revolvers—all at once there were revolvers in the dream—and joyously put the Gods to death.

From each day's dawn to dusk each night a leopard, during the final years of the twelfth century, beheld a few boards, some vertical iron bars, shifting men and women, a thick wall, and perhaps a stone gutter stopped with dry leaves. He did not know, he could not know, that what he longed for was love and cruelty and the hot pleasure of tearing things apart and the wind carrying the scent of a deer. But something in him was smothering and rebelling, and God spoke to him in a dream: "You live and will die in this cage so that a man known to me may look at you a predetermined number of times, and may not forget you, and may put your shape and your symbol in a poem which has its necessary place in the scheme of the universe. You suffer captivity, but you will have given a word to the poem." God, in the dream, illumined the animal's brutishness and he understood the reasons, and accepted his destiny; but when he awoke there was only a dark resignation in him, a valiant ignorance, for the machinery of the world is far too complex for the simplicity of a wild beast.

Years later Dante lay dying in Ravenna, as unjustified and as alone as any other man. In a dream God declared to him the secret purpose of his life and his work; Dante, filled with wonder, knew at last who he was and what he was, and he blessed his bitter sufferings. Tradition has it that, on waking, he felt he had been given—and then had lost—something infinite, something he would not be able to recover, or even to glimpse, for the machinery of the world is far too complex for the simplicity of men.

Borges and I

It's the other one, it's Borges, that things happen to. I stroll about Buenos Aires and stop, perhaps mechanically now, to look at the arch of an entrance or an iron gate. News of Borges reaches me through the mail and I see his name on an academic ballot or in a biographical dictionary. I like hourglasses, maps, eighteenth-century typography, the taste of coffee, and Stevenson's prose. The other one shares these preferences with me, but in a vain way that converts them into the attributes of an actor. It would be too much to say that our relations are hostile; I live, I allow myself to live, so that Borges may contrive his literature and that literature justifies my existence. I do not mind confessing that he has managed to write some worthwhile pages, but those pages cannot save me, perhaps because the good part no longer belongs to anyone, not even to the other one, but rather to the Spanish language or to tradition. Otherwise, I am destined to be lost, definitively, and only a few instants of me will be able to survive in the other one. Little by little I am yielding him everything, although I am well aware of his perverse habit of falsifying and exaggerating. Spinoza held that all things long to preserve their own nature: the rock wants to be rock forever and the tiger, a tiger. But I must live on in Borges, not in myself—if indeed I am anyone—though I recognize myself less in his books than in many others, or than in the laborious strumming of a guitar. Years ago I tried to free myself from him and I passed from lower-middle-class myths to playing games with time and infinity, but those games are Borges' now, and I will have to conceive something else. Thus my life is running away, and I lose everything and everything belongs to oblivion, or to the other one.

I do not know which of us two is writing this page.

PART TWO

Translated by Harold Morland

Poem about Gifts

Let none think I by tear or reproach make light
Of this manifesting the mastery
Of God, who with excelling irony
Gives me at once both books and night.

In this city of books he made these eyes
The sightless rulers who can only read,
In libraries of dreams, the pointless
Paragraphs each new dawn offers

To awakened care. In vain the day
Squanders on them its infinite books,
As difficult as the difficult scripts
That perished in Alexandria.

An old Greek story tells how some king died
Of hunger and thirst, though proffered springs and fruits;
My bearings lost, I trudge from side to side
Of this lofty, long blind library.

The walls present, but uselessly,
Encyclopaedia, atlas, Orient
And the West, all centuries, dynasties,
Symbols, cosmos, and cosmogonies.

Slow in my darkness, I explore
The hollow gloom with my hesitant stick,
I, that used to figure Paradise
In such a library's guise.

Something that surely cannot be called
Mere *chance* must rule these things;
Some other man has met this doom
On other days of many books and the dark.

As I walk through the slow galleries
I grow to feel with a kind of holy dread
That I am that other, I am the dead,
And the steps I make are also his.

Which of us two is writing now these lines
About a plural I and a single gloom?
What does it matter what word is my name
If the curse is indivisibly the same?

Groussac or Borges, I gaze at this beloved
World that grows more shapeless, and its light
Dies down into a pale, uncertain ash
Resembling sleep and the oblivion of night.

The Hourglass

It is well that time can be measured
With the harsh shadow a column in summer
Casts, or the water of that river
In which Heraclitus saw our folly,

Since both to time and destiny
The two seem alike: the unweighable daytime
Shadow, and the irrevocable course
Of water following its own path.

It is well, but time in the desert
Found another substance, smooth and heavy,
That seems to have been imagined
For measuring dead men's time.

Hence the allegorical instrument
Of the dictionary illustrations,
The thing that gray antiquaries
Will consign to the red-ash world

Of the odd chess-bishop, of the sword
Defenseless, of the telescope bleared,
Of sandalwood eroded by opium,
Of dust, of hazard, of the *nada*.

Who has not paused before the severe
And sullen instrument accompanying
The scythe in the god's right hand
Whose outlines Duerer etched?

Through the open apex the inverted cone
Lets the minute sand fall down,
Gradual gold that loosens itself and fills
The concave crystal of its universe.

There is pleasure in watching the recondite
Sand that slides away and slopes
And, at the falling-point, piles up
With an urgency wholly human.

The sand of the cycles is the same,
And infinite, the history of sand;
Thus, deep beneath your joys and pain
Unwoundable eternity is still the abyss.

Never is there a halt in the fall.
It is I lose blood, not the glass. The ceremony
Of drawing off the sand goes on forever
And with the sand our life is leaving us.

In the minutes of the sand I believe
I feel the cosmic time: the history
That memory locks up in its mirrors
Or that magic Lethe has dissolved.

The pillar of smoke and the pillar of fire,
Carthage and Rome and their crushing war,
Simon Magus, the seven feet of earth
That the Saxon proffered the Norway king,

This tireless subtle thread of unnumbered
Sand degrades all down to loss.
I cannot save myself, a come-by-chance
Of time, being matter that is crumbling.

The Game of Chess

In their grave corner, the players
Deploy the slow pieces. And the chessboard
Detains them until dawn in its severe
Compass in which two colors hate each other.

Within it the shapes give off a magic
Strength: Homeric tower, and nimble
Horse, a fighting queen, a backward king,
A bishop on the bias, and aggressive pawns.

When the players have departed, and
When time has consumed them utterly,
The ritual will not have ended.

That war first flamed out in the east
Whose amphitheatre is now the world.
And like the other, this game is infinite.

II

Slight king, oblique bishop, and a queen
Blood-lusting; upright tower, crafty pawn—
Over the black and the white of their path
They foray and deliver armed battle.

They do not know it is the artful hand
Of the player that rules their fate,
They do not know that an adamant rigor
Subdues their free will and their span.

But the player likewise is a prisoner
(The maxim is Omar's) on another board
Of dead-black nights and of white days.

God moves the player and he, the piece.
What god behind God originates the scheme
Of dust and time and dream and agony?

Mirrors

I, who felt the horror of mirrors
Not only in front of the impenetrable crystal
Where there ends and begins, uninhabitable,
An impossible space of reflections,

But of gazing even on water that mimics
The other blue in its depth of sky,
That at times gleams back the illusory flight
Of the inverted bird, or that ripples,

And in front of the silent surface
Of subtle ebony whose polish shows
Like a repeating dream the white
Of something marble or something rose,

Today at the tip of so many and perplexing
Wandering years under the varying moon,
I ask myself what whim of fate
Made me so fearful of a glancing mirror.

Mirrors in metal, and the masked
Mirror of mahogany that in its mist
Of a red twilight hazes
The face that is gazed on as it gazes,

I see them as infinite, elemental
Executors of an ancient pact,
To multiply the world like the act
Of begetting. Sleepless. Bringing doom.

They prolong this hollow, unstable world
In their dizzying spider's-web;
Sometimes in the afternoon they are blurred
By the breath of a man who is not dead.

The crystal spies on us. If within the four
Walls of a bedroom a mirror stares,
I'm no longer alone. There is someone there.
In the dawn reflections mutely stage a show.

Everything happens and nothing is recorded
In these rooms of the looking glass,
Where, magicked into rabbis, we
Now read the books from right to left.

Claudius, king of an afternoon, a dreaming king,
Did not feel it a dream until that day
When an actor showed the world his crime
In a tableau, silently in mime.

It is strange to dream, and to have mirrors
Where the commonplace, worn-out repertory
Of every day may include the illusory
Profound globe that reflections scheme.

God (I keep thinking) has taken pains
To design that ungraspable architecture
Reared by every dawn from the gleam
Of a mirror, by darkness from a dream.

God has created nighttime, which he arms
With dreams, and mirrors, to make clear
To man he is a reflection and a mere
Vanity. Therefore these alarms.

All things she possessed and slowly
All things left her. We have seen her
Armed with loveliness. The morning
And the strenuous midday showed her,
At her summit, the handsome kingdoms
Of the earth. The afternoon was clouding them.
The friendly stars (the infinite
And ubiquitous mesh of causes) granted her
That wealth which annuls all distance
Like the magic carpet, and which makes
Desire and possession one; and a skill in verse
That transforms our actual sorrows
Into a music, a hearsay, and a symbol;
And granted fervor, and into her blood the battle
Of Ituzaingó and the heaviness of laurels;
And the joy of losing herself in the wandering
River of time (river and labyrinth),
And in the slow tints of afternoons.
All things left her, all
But one. Her highborn courtliness
Accompanied her to the end of the journey,
Beyond the rapture and its eclipse,
In a way like an angel's. Of Elvira
The first thing that I saw, such years ago,
Was her smile and also it was the last.

Susana Soca

With slow love she looked at the scattered
Colors of afternoon. It pleased her
To lose herself in intricate melody
Or in the curious life of verses.
Not elemental red but the grays
Spun her delicate destiny,
Fashioned to discriminate and exercised
In vacillation and in blended tints.
Without venturing to tread this perplexing
Labyrinth, she watched from without
The shapes of things, their tumult and their course,
Just like that other lady of the mirror.
Gods who dwell far-off past prayer
Abandoned her to that tiger, Fire.

The Moon

History tells us how in that past time
When all things happened, real,
Imaginary, and dubious, a man
Conceived the unconscionable plan

Of making an abridgement of the universe
In a single book and with infinite zest
He towered his screed up, lofty and
Strenuous, polished it, spoke the final verse.

About to offer his thanks to fortune,
He lifted up his eyes and saw a burnished
Disc in the air and realized, stunned,
That somehow he had forgotten the moon.

The story I have told, although a tale,
Can represent the witching spell
So many of us use when at our craft
Of transmuting our life into words.

The essence is always lost. This is the one
Law of every word about inspiration.
Nor will this summary of mine avoid it
About my long traffic with the moon.

Where I saw it first I could not tell,
If in an earlier heaven than the teaching
Of the Greek, or some evening when it was reaching
Over the patio fig tree and the well.

As we know, this life being mutable
Can be, among many things, so beautiful
Because it brings some afternoon, with her,
The chance to gaze at you, oh varying moon.

But more than moons of the night I can
Remember those in verse: like that enchanted
Dragon moon so horrible in the ballad,
And then Quevedo with his moon of blood.

Of another moon of blood and scarlet
John spoke in his book about the ferocious
Monsters and their revelries;
And other clear moons with a silver sheen.

Pythagoras (so tradition tells)
Wrote words of blood on a looking glass
That men could read with the naked eye
Reflected in that mirror in the sky.

And there's a forest of iron where lurks
The enormous wolf whose destiny
Is to shatter the moon and do it to death
When the last dawn reddens the sea.

(Of this the prophetic North is aware
And how on that day the opened seas
Through all the world will be scoured by a ship
Fashioned of dead men's nails.)

When in Geneva or Zurich fortune willed
That I should be a poet too,
I secretly assumed, as poets do,
The duty on me to define the moon.

With a sort of studious pain
I ran through modest variations,
With the lively dread Lugones already
Had made the amber or sand his own.

Of faraway ivory, smoke, and the cold
Of snows were the moons that lit
My verses, which certainly were not fit
For the difficult honor of reaching print.

I thought of the poet as being that man
Who, like red Adam in Paradise,
Lays down for everything its precise
And exact and not-known name.

Ariosto taught me that in the shifting
Moon are the dreams, the ungraspable,
Time that is lost, the possible
Or the impossible, which are the same.

Apollodorus let me descry
The magical shade of triform Diana;
And Hugo gave me a golden sickle,
An Irishman, his tragic obscure moon.

And, while I sounded the depths of that mine
Of mythology's moons, just here
At the turn of a corner I could see
The celestial moon of every day.

Among all words I knew there is one
With power to record and re-present.
The secret, I see, is with humble intent
To use it simply. *Moon.*

Now I shall never dare to stain
Its pure appearing with a futile image;
I see it indecipherable and daily
And out of reach of my literature.

I know that the moon or the word *moon*
Is a letter that was created to share
In the complex scripture of that rare
Thing that we are, both manifold and one.

It is one of those symbols given to man
By fate or chance, which one day he
May use to write his own true name,
Uplifted in glory or in agony.

The Rain

The afternoon grows light because at last
Abruptly a minutely shredded rain
Is falling, or it fell. For once again
Rain is something happening in the past.

Whoever hears it fall has brought to mind
Time when by a sudden lucky chance
A flower called "rose" was open to his glance
And the curious color of the colored kind.

This rain that blinds the windows with its mists
Will gladden in suburbs no more to be found
The black grapes on a vine there overhead

In a certain patio that no longer exists.
And the drenched afternoon brings back the sound
How longed for, of my father's voice, not dead.

On the Effigy of a Captain in Cromwell's Armies

The battlements of Mars no longer yield
To him whom choiring angels now inspire;
And from another light (and age) entire
Those eyes look down that viewed the battlefield.
Your hand is on the metal of your sword.
And through the green shires war stalks on his way;
They wait beyond that gloom with England still,
Your mount, your march, your glory of the Lord.
Captain, your eager cares were all deceits,
Vain was your armor, vain the stubborn will
Of man, whose term is but a little day;
Time has the conquests, man has the defeats.
The steel that was to wound you fell to rust;
And you (as we shall be) are turned to dust.

To an Old Poet

You walk the Castile countryside
As if you hardly saw that it was there.
A tricky verse of John's your only care,
You scarcely notice that the sun has died

In a yellow glow. The light diffuses, trembles,
And on the borders of the East there spreads
That moon of mockery which most resembles
The mirror of Wrath, a moon of scarlet-reds.

You raise your eyes and look. You seem to note
A something of your own that like a bud
Half-breaks then dies. You bend your pallid head

And sadly make your way—the moment fled—
And with it, unrecalled, what once you wrote:
And for his epitaph a moon of blood.

The Other Tiger

And the craft that createth a semblance
MORRIS: SIGURD THE VOLSUNG (1876)

I think of a tiger. The gloom here makes
The vast and busy Library seem lofty
And pushes the shelves back;
Strong, innocent, covered with blood and new,
It will move through its forest and its morning
And will print its tracks on the muddy
Margins of a river whose name it does not know
(In its world there are no names nor past
Nor time to come, only the fixed moment)
And will overleap barbarous distances
And will scent out of the plaited maze
Of all the scents the scent of dawn
And the delighting scent of the deer.
Between the stripes of the bamboo I decipher
Its stripes and have the feel of the bony structure
That quivers under the glowing skin.
In vain do the curving seas intervene
And the deserts of the planet;
From this house in a far-off port
In South America, I pursue and dream you,
O tiger on the Ganges' banks.
In my soul the afternoon grows wider and I reflect
That the tiger invoked in my verse
Is a ghost of a tiger, a symbol,
A series of literary tropes
And memories from the encyclopaedia
And not the deadly tiger, the fateful jewel
That, under the sun or the varying moon,
In Sumatra or Bengal goes on fulfilling
Its round of love, of idleness and death.
To the symbolic tiger I have opposed
The real thing, with its warm blood,
That decimates the tribe of buffaloes
And today, the third of August, '59,
Stretches on the grass a deliberate

Shadow, but already the fact of naming it
And conjecturing its circumstance
Makes it a figment of art and no creature
Living among those that walk the earth.

We shall seek a third tiger. This
Will be like those others a shape
Of my dreaming, a system of words
A man makes and not the vertebrate tiger
That, beyond the mythologies,
Is treading the earth. I know well enough
That something lays on me this quest
Undefined, senseless and ancient, and I go on
Seeking through the afternoon time
The other tiger, that which is not in verse.

Blind Pew

Far from the sea and from fine war,
Which love hauled with him now that they were lost,
The blind old buccaneer was trudging
The cloddy roads of the English countryside.

Barked at by the farmhouse curs,
The butt of all the village lads,
In sickly and broken sleep he stirred
The black dust in the wayside ditches.

He knew that golden beaches far away
Kept hidden for him his own treasure,
So cursing fate's not worth the breath;

You too on golden beaches far away
Keep for yourself an incorruptible treasure:
Hazy, many-peopled death.

Referring to a Ghost of
Eighteen Hundred and Ninety-Odd

Nothing. Only Muraña's knife.
Only in the gray afternoon the story cut short.
I don't know why in the afternoons I'm companioned
By this assassin that I've never seen.
Palermo was further down. The yellow
Thick wall of the jail dominated
Suburb and mud flat. Through this savage
District went the sordid knife.
The knife. The face has been smudged out
And of that hired fellow whose austere
Craft was courage, nothing remained
But a ghost and a gleam of steel.
May time, that sullies marble statues,
Salvage this staunch name: Juan Muraña.

Referring to the Death of
Colonel Francisco Borges (1835–1874)

I leave him on his horse, and in the gray
And twilit hour he fixed with death for a meeting;
Of all the hours that shaped his human day
May this last long, though bitter and defeating.
The whiteness of his horse and poncho over
The plain advances. Setting sights again
To the hollow rifles death lies under cover.
Francisco Borges sadly crosses the plain.
This that encircled him, the rifles' rattle,
This that he saw, the pampa without bounds,
Had been his life, his sum of sights and sounds.
His every-dailiness is here and in the battle.
I leave him lofty in his epic universe
Almost as if not tolled for by my verse.

In Memoriam : A. R.

Vague chance or the precise laws
That govern this dream, the universe,
Granted me to share a smooth
Stretch of the course with Alfonso Reyes.

He knew well that art which no one
Wholly knows, neither Sindbad nor Ulysses,
Which is to pass from one land on to others
And yet to be entirely in each one.

If memory ever did with its arrow
Pierce him, he fashioned with the intense
Metal of the weapon the rhythmical, slow
Alexandrine or the grieving dirge.

In his labors he was helped by mankind's
Hope, which was the light of his life,
To create a line that is not to be forgotten
And to renew Castilian prose.

Beyond the Mio Cid with slow gait
And that flock of folk that strive to be obscure,
He tracked the fugitive literature
As far as the suburbs of the city slang.

In the five gardens of the Marino
He delayed, but he had something in him
Immortal, of the essence which preferred
Arduous studies and diviner duties.

To put it better, he preferred the gardens
Of meditation, where Porphyry
Reared before the shadows and delight
The Tree of the Beginning and the End.

Reyes, meticulous providence
That governs the prodigal and the thrifty
Gave some of us the sector or the arc,
But to you the whole circumference.

You sought the happy and the sad
That fame or frontispieces hide;
Like the God of Erigena you desired
To be no man so that you might be all.

Vast and delicate splendors
Your style attained, that manifest rose,
And turned that fighting blood of your forebears
Into cheerful blood to wage in God's own wars.

Where (I ask) will the Mexican be?
Will he contemplate with Oedipus' horror
Before the stranger Sphinx, the unmoving
Archetype of Visage and of Hand?

Or is he wandering, as Swedenborg says,
Through a world more vivid and complex
Than our earthly one, which is scarcely the reflex
Of that high, celestial something impenetrable?

If (as the empires of lacquer
And ebony teach) man's memory shapes
Its own Eden within, there is now in glory
One Mexico more, another Cuernavaca.

God knows the colors that fate
Has in store for man beyond his day;
I walk these streets—and yet how little
Do I catch up with the meaning of death.

One thing alone I know. That Alfonso Reyes
(Wherever the sea has brought him safe ashore)
Will apply himself happy and watchful
To other enigmas and to other laws.

Let us honor with the palms and the shout
Of victory the peerless and unique;
No tears must shame the verse
Our love inscribes to his name.

The Borges

I know little—or nothing—of my own forebears;
The Borges back in Portugal; vague folk
That in my flesh, obscurely, still evoke
Their customs, and their firmnesses and fears.
As slight as if they'd never lived in the sun
And free from any trafficking with art,
They form an indecipherable part
Of time, of earth, and of oblivion.
And better so. For now, their labors past,
They're Portugal, they are that famous race
Who forced the shining ramparts of the East,
And launched on seas, and seas of sand as wide.
The king they are in mystic desert place,
Once lost; they're one who swears he has not died.

To Luís de Camoëns

Without lament or anger time will nick
The most heroic swords. Poor and in sorrow,
You came home to a land turned from tomorrow,
O captain, came to die within her, sick,
And with her. In the magic desert-wastes
The flower of Portugal was lost and died,
And the harsh Spaniard, hitherto subdued,
Was menacing her naked, open coasts.
I wish I knew if on this hither side
Of the ultimate shore you humbly understood
That all that was lost, the Western Hemisphere
And the Orient, the steel and banner dear,
Would still live on (from human change set free)
In your epic *Lusiados* timelessly.

Nineteen Hundred and Twenty-Odd

The wheeling of the stars is not infinite
And the tiger is one of the forms that return,
But we, remote from chance or hazard,
Believed we were exiled in a time outworn,
Time when nothing can happen.
The universe, the tragic universe, was not here
And maybe should be looked for somewhere else;
I hatched a humble mythology of fencing
                          walls and knives
And Ricardo thought of his drovers.

We did not know that time to come held a lightning bolt;
We did not foresee the shame, the fire, and the fearful
                          night of the Alliance;
Nothing told us that Argentine history would be thrust
                          out to walk the streets,
History, indignation, love,
The multitudes like the sea, the name of Córdoba,
The flavor of the real and the incredible, the
                          horror and the glory.

Ode Composed in 1960

Sheer accident or the secret laws
That rule this dream, my destiny,
Will—O needed and sweet homeland
That not without glory and without shame embrace
A hundred and fifty arduous years—
That I, the drop, should speak with you, the river,
That I, the instant, speak with you, who are time,
And that the intimate dialogue resort,
As the custom is, to the rites and the dark hints
Beloved of the gods, and to the decorum of verse.

My country, I have sensed you in the tumbledown
Decadence of the widespread suburbs,
And in that thistledown that the pampas wind
Blows into the entrance hall, and in the patient rain,
And in the slow coursing of the stars,
And in the hand that tunes a guitar,
And in the gravitation of the plain
That, from however far, our blood feels
As the Briton feels the sea, and in the pious
Symbols and urns of a vault,
And in the gallant love of jasmine,
And in the silver of a picture-frame and the polished
Rubbing of the silent mahogany,
And in the flavors of meat and fruits,
And in a flag sort of blue and white
Over a barracks, and in unappetizing stories
Of street-corner knifings, and in the sameness
Of afternoons that are wiped out and leave us,
And in the vague pleased memory
Of patios with slaves bearing
The name of their masters, and in the poor
Leaves of certain books for the blind
That fire scattered, and in the fall
Of those epic rains in September
That nobody will forget—but these things
Are not wholly you yourself nor yet your symbols.

You are more than your wide territory
And more than the days of your unmeasured time,
You are more than the unimaginable sum
Of your children after you. We do not know
What you are for God in the living
Heart of the eternal archetypes,
But by this imperfectly glimpsed visage
We live and die and have our being—

O never-from-me and mystery-my-country.

No man can write a book. Because
Before a book can truly be
It needs the rise and set of the sun,
Centuries, arms, and the binding and sundering sea.

So Ariosto thought, who to the slow pleasure
Gave himself, in the leisure of roads
With shining statuary and black pines,
Of dreaming again on things already dreamed.

The air of his own Italy was dense
With dreams, which recalling and forgetting,
With shapes of war that through harsh centuries
Wearied the land, plaited and schemed.

A legion that lost itself in the valleys
Of Aquitaine into ambush fell;
And thus was born that dream of a sword
And a horn that cried in Roncesvalles.

Over English orchards the brutal Saxon
Spread his armies and his idols
In a stubborn, clenching war; and of these things
A dream was left behind called Arthur.

From the northern islands, with the blind
Sun blurring the sea, there came
The dream of a virgin, waiting in sleep
For her lord, within a ring of flame.

From Persia or Parnassus—who knows where?—
That dream of an armed enchanter driving
A winged steed through the startled air
And suddenly into the western desert diving.

As if from this enchanter's steed
Ariosto saw the kingdoms of the earth
All furrowed by war's revelry
And by young love intent to prove his worth.

As if through a delicate golden mist
He saw a garden in the world that reached
Beyond its hedge into other intimacies
For Angelica's and Medoro's love.

Like the illusory splendors that in Hindustan
Opium leaves on the rim of sight,
The Furioso's loves go shimmering by
In the kaleidoscope of his delight.

Neither of love nor irony unaware,
He dreamed like this, in a modest style,
Of a strange lone castle; and all things there
(As in this life) were the devil's guile.

As to every poet what may chance—
Or fate allot as a private doom—
He traveled the roads to Ferrara
And, at the same time, walked the moon.

The dross of dreams that have no shape—
The mud that the Nile of sleep leaves by—
With the stuff of these for skein, he'd move
Through that gleaming labyrinth and escape;

Through this great diamond, in which a man
May lose himself by the hap of the game,
In the whereness of music drowsing,
Be beside himself in flesh and name.

Europe entire was lost. By the working
Of that ingenious and malicious art,
Milton could weep for Brandimarte's
Death and Dolinda's anguished heart.

Europe was lost. But other gifts were given
By that vast dream to fame's true scions
That dwell in the deserts of the East,
And the night that was full of lions.

The delectable book that still enchants
Tells of a king who, at morning's star,
Surrenders his queen of the night
Before the implacable scimitar.

Wings that are shaggy night, and cruel
Claws that an elephant grip,
Magnetic mountains that with loving
Embrace can shatter a ship,

The earth sustained by a bull, the bull
By a fish; abracadabras, and old
Talismans and mystic words
That in granite open caves of gold;

This the Saracen people dreamt
Who followed Agramante's crest;
This the turban'd faces dreamed
And the dream now lords it over the West.

And Orlando is now a region that smiles,
A country of the mind for miles
Of wonders in abandoned dreams;
And not even finally smiles, but seems—

By the skill of Islam, brought so low
To fable merely and scholarship,
It stands alone, dreaming itself. (And glory
Is oblivion shaped into a story.)

Through the window, paling now, the quivering
Light of one more evening touches the book
And once again the gilding on the cover
Glows and once again it fades.

In the deserted room the silent
Book still journeys into time. And leaves
Behind it—dawns, night-watching hours,
My own life too, this quickening dream.

At fifty generations' end
(And such abysses time affords us all)
I return to the further shore of a great river
That the vikings' dragons did not reach,
To the harsh and arduous words
That, with a mouth now turned to dust,
I used in my Northumbrian, Mercian days
Before I became a Haslam or Borges.
On Saturday we read that Julius Caesar
Was the first man out of Romeburg to strip the
veil from England;
Before the clusters swell again on the vine
I shall have heard the voice of the nightingale
With its enigma, and the elegy of the warrior twelve
That surround the tomb of their king.
Symbols of other symbols, variations
On the English or German future seem these words to me
That once on a time were images
A man made use of praising the sea or a sword;
Tomorrow they will live again,
Tomorrow *fyr* will not be *fire* but that form
Of a tamed and changing god
It has been given to none to see without an ancient dread.

Praised be the infinite
Mesh of effects and causes
Which, before it shows me the mirror
In which I shall see no-one or I shall see another,
Grants me now this contemplation pure
Of a language of the dawn.

Gentile or Hebrew or simply a man
Whose face has now been lost in time;
From oblivion we shall not redeem
The silent letters of his name.

Of clemency he knew no more
Than a robber whom Judea nails
To a cross. The time that went before
We cannot reach. But in his final

Job of dying crucified,
He heard among the gibes of the crowd,
That the fellow dying at his side
Was a god, and so he said to him, blind:

"Remember me when you shall come
Into your kingdom," and the unconceivable voice
That one day will be judge of all mankind
Made promise, from the terrible Cross,

Of Paradise. And they said nothing more
Until the end came, but the pride
Of history will not let die the memory
Of that afternoon when these two died.

O friends, the innocence of this friend
Of Jesus Christ, this candor which made him
Ask for his Paradise and gain it so,
Even in the shame of punishment,

Is the same that many a time has brought
The sinner to sin—as it chanced, to murder.

Adrogué

Let no fear be that in indecipherable night
I shall lose myself among the black flowers
Of the park, where the secret bird that sings
The same song over and over, the round pond,

And the summerhouse, and the indistinct
Statue and the hazardous ruin, weave
Their scheme of things propitious to the languor
Of afternoons and to nostalgic loves.

Hollow in the hollow shade, the coachhouse
Marks (I know) the tremulous confines
Of this world of dust and jasmine,
Pleasing to Verlaine, pleasing to Julio Herrera.

The eucalyptus trees bestow on the gloom
Their medicinal smell: that ancient smell
That, beyond all time and the ambiguity
Of language, speaks of manorhouse time.

My footstep seeks and finds the hoped-for
Threshold. The flat roof there defines
Its darkened edge, and in measured time the tap
In the checkered patio slowly drips.

On the other side of the door they sleep,
Those who by means of dreams
In the visionary darkness are masters
Of the long yesterday and of all things dead.

I know every single object of this old
Building: the flakes of mica
On that gray stone that doubles itself
Endlessly in the smudgy mirror

And the lion's head that bites
A ring and the stained-glass windows
That reveal to a child wonders
Of a crimson world and another greener world.

For beyond all chance and death
They endure, each one with its history,
But all this is happening in that destiny
Of a fourth dimension, which is memory.

In that and there alone now still exist
The patios and the gardens. And the past
Holds them in that forbidden round
Embracing at one time vesper and dawn.

How could I lose that precise
Order of humble and beloved things,
As out of reach today as the roses
That Paradise gave to the first Adam?

The ancient amazement of the elegy
Loads me down when I think of that house
And I do not understand how time goes by,
I, who am time and blood and agony.

Ars Poetica

To gaze at the river made of time and water
And recall that time itself is another river,
To know we cease to be, just like the river,
And that our faces pass away, just like the water.

To feel that waking is another sleep
That dreams it does not sleep and that death,
Which our flesh dreads, is that very death
Of every night, which we call sleep.

To see in the day or in the year a symbol
Of mankind's days and of his years,
To transform the outrage of the years
Into a music, a rumor and a symbol,

To see in death a sleep, and in the sunset
A sad gold, of such is Poetry
Immortal and a pauper. For Poetry
Returns like the dawn and the sunset.

At times in the afternoons a face
Looks at us from the depths of a mirror;
Art must be like that mirror
That reveals to us this face of ours.

They tell how Ulysses, glutted with wonders,
Wept with love to descry his Ithaca
Humble and green. Art is that Ithaca
Of green eternity, not of wonders.

It is also like an endless river
That passes and remains, a mirror for one same
Inconstant Heraclitus, who is the same
And another, like an endless river.

Museum

On Rigor in Science

. . . In that Empire, the Art of Cartography reached such Perfection that the map of one Province alone took up the whole of a City, and the map of the empire, the whole of a Province. In time, those Unconscionable Maps did not satisfy and the Colleges of Cartographers set up a Map of the Empire which had the size of the Empire itself and coincided with it point by point. Less Addicted to the Study of Cartography, Succeeding Generations understood that this Widespread Map was Useless and not without Impiety they abandoned it to the Inclemencies of the Sun and of the Winters. In the deserts of the West some mangled Ruins of the Map lasted on, inhabited by Animals and Beggars; in the whole Country there are no other relics of the Disciplines of Geography.

Suarez Miranda: *Viajes de Varones Prudentes,*
Book Four, Chapter XLV, Lérida, 1658.

Quatrain

Others died, but it happened in the past,
The season (as all men know) most favorable for death.
Is it possible that I, subject of Yaqub Almansur,
Must die as roses had to die and Aristotle?

From Divan of Almoqtadir El Magrebi (12th century)

Limits

There is a line in Verlaine I shall not recall again,
There is a street close by forbidden to my feet,
There's a mirror that's seen me for the very last time,
There is a door that I have locked till the end of the world.
Among the books in my library (I have them before me)
There are some that I shall never open now.
This summer I complete my fiftieth year;
Death is gnawing at me ceaselessly.

Julio Platero Haedo: *Inscripciones* (Montevideo, 1923)

The Poet Declares His Renown

The circle of the sky metes out my glory,
The libraries of the East contend for my poems,
Emirs seek me out to fill my mouth with gold,
Angels already know by heart my latest ghazal.
My working tools are humiliation and an anguish;
Would to God I'd been stillborn.

From the Divan of Abulcasim El Hadrami (12th century)

91

The Magnanimous Enemy

Magnus Barfod, in the year 1102, undertook the general conquest of the kingdoms of Ireland; it is said that on the eve of his death he received this greeting from Muirchertach, king in Dublin:

May gold and the storm fight along with you in your armies,
                           Magnus Barfod.
Tomorrow, in the fields of my kingdom, may you have a
                           happy battle.
May your kingly hands be terrible in weaving the sword-stuff.
May those opposing your sword become meat for the red swan.
May your many gods glut you with glory, may they glut you
                           with blood.
Victorious may you be in the dawn, king who tread on Ireland.
Of your many days may none shine bright as tomorrow.
Because that day will be the last. I swear it to you,
                           King Magnus.
For before its light is blotted, I shall vanquish you and blot you
                         out, Magnus Barfod.

From H. Gering: *Anhang zur Heimskringla* (1893)

The Regret of Heraclitus

I, who have been so many men, have never been
The one in whose embrace Matilde Urbach swooned.

Gaspar Camerarius, in *Deliciae poetarum Borussiae*, VII, 16

Epilogue

God grant that the essential monotony of this miscellany (which time has compiled—not I—and which admits past pieces that I have not dared to revise, because I wrote them with a different concept of literature) be less evident than the geographical and historical diversity of its themes. Of all the books I have delivered to the presses, none, I think, is as personal as the straggling collection mustered for this hodge-podge, precisely because it abounds in reflections and inter-polations. Few things have happened to me, and I have read a great many. Or rather, few things have happened to me more worth remembering than Schopenhauer's thought or the music of England's words.

A man sets himself the task of portraying the world. Through the years he peoples a space with images of prov-inces, kingdoms, mountains, bays, ships, islands, fishes, rooms, instruments, stars, horses, and people. Shortly before his death, he discovers that that patient labyrinth of lines traces the image of his face.

J. L. B.

Buenos Aires, October 31, 1960.

Appendix

Some Facts in the Life of Jorge Luis Borges

Jorge Luis Borges was born in Buenos Aires, August 24, 1899. While he was still very young, his parents took him to Europe, where he lived from 1914 to 1921. After completion of his secondary schooling in Geneva he moved to Spain (1918). He traveled throughout the Mother Country, residing chiefly in Mallorca, Seville, and Madrid. His first known poem, published in the Madrid periodical *Grecia*, dates from 1919. In Spain he was in close touch with the young vanguardist poets, especially those of the so-called *ultraísta* group. In 1921 Borges returned to Buenos Aires, where he was quickly recognized as one of the principal poets of the rebellious Argentine vanguard. The works to which this reputation is due are three books of poetry: *Fervor de Buenos Aires* (1923), *Luna de enfrente* (1925), and *Cuaderno San Martín* (1929). In subsequent years he has lived in Buenos Aires, continually and now permanently. His personal life was obscure and tranquil, as befits a suburban municipal librarian. Paradoxically, literary circles increasingly lionized the modest librarian. He was a frequent contributor to *Sur*, the great literary and cultural review edited by Victoria Ocampo.

In the early thirties his literary activity tended more and more away from verse and toward the essay and the story. Of this phase of his work *Historia universal de la infamia* (1935) is the author's most representative book. But his best narratives did not appear in collected form until 1944, when they were grouped under the title *Ficciones*. This is the book to which Borges owes his international fame. His stories have become known in translation throughout Europe, especially in France. *Ficciones* was followed by another similar collection, *El Aleph* (1949).

In 1961, as the crowning mark of international recognition of his work's importance and quality, he received the *Prix International des Editeurs*, which he shared with Samuel Beckett.

A lover of freedom, though unaffiliated with political groups or parties, Borges opposed the Perón dictatorship. The dictator retaliated by attempting to humiliate him, relieving him of his modest post as librarian and naming him poultry inspector. After the fall of General Perón the Argentine government, in a desire to attest to his compatriots' gratitude for his valorous attitude during the difficult years, made him director of the National Library of Argentina, a position he holds to the present. Borges also teaches courses in English literature at the University of Buenos Aires.

At the invitation of the Tinker Foundation, in 1961, Jorge Luis Borges came to The University of Texas, where he gave courses in Argentine literature from September to January of the following year. He traveled extensively in the United States in 1962, lecturing at leading universities. In 1963 he returned to Europe. His present residence is in Argentina.

Other works of Borges which should be mentioned are: *Poemas, 1923–1958, Inquisiciones* (1925), *Evaristo Carriego* (1930), *Discusión* (1932), *Antiguas literaturas germánicas* (1951), *Otras inquisiciones, 1937–1952,* and *Historia de la eternidad* (1953).